E-BIKES

Putting the fun Back Into Cycling (*and Life*) at any age

BY DAVE HOGAN

Author of the Blogs *This Retirement Life* and *This E-Bike Life*

E-bikes - Putting the fun Back Into Cycling (and Life) at any age

By Dave Hogan
© 2021, DaHogan LLC

Book design by Cristina Miller, Nine31 Creative

Paperback: 978-1-7379275-1-8
Hardback: 978-1-7379275-2-5
E-Book: 978-1-7379275-0-1

Table of Contents

Foreword

As a child growing up in the 1950s and 1960s, my bicycle was my constant companion. I ran errands for my parents to the neighborhood Big Star supermarket and Rexall drug store. I rode my bike to school. My bike helped me explore nearby parks and neighborhoods.

In a word, my beloved bicycle gave me freedom and adventure. I was at my happiest when riding my bike.

I suspect many of you who are part of the Baby Boomer generation have similar fond memories of time spent as a child on your bicycle. Whether your childhood bike sported a banana seat and high handlebars, or white wall tires and streamers, it was special to you.

But just like Little Jackie Paper outgrew his need for Puff the Magic Dragon, somewhere along the way many of us discarded our bicycles as we turned our attention to cars and trucks and all of the demands of adulthood.

Now that Baby Boomers are reaching retirement age and thinking more about travel and staying active, the bicycle has come back into our lives. For many of us who are now senior adults (or at least AARP says we are), our old romance with the bicycle has re-blossomed. We're in love all over again.

This time, however, we're not carefree kids anymore. Even if we still feel like kids sometimes, our bodies tell us differently. Age takes its toll. While it may have been fun to grunt and sweat up hills on our bikes back in the day, that's not something we look forward to doing today as mature adults. Whether it's aching joints, cardiovascular weakness, or breathing difficulties, pedaling a traditional bike is much harder for us now than when we were young and invincible.

Thankfully, a new type of bike has emerged just in time for our aging, aching bodies. It's the electric bike. For seniors, e-bikes are a game-changer. With an e-bike (or an electric trike), most seniors can successfully ride a bicycle well into old age. Thousands of riders in their 80s still enjoy cycling on a regular basis. Even some seniors who have trouble walking more than a few blocks have no trouble pedaling an e-bike for several miles at a time.

This book focuses on the cycling needs of my fellow Baby Boomers, but really anyone of any age who is interested in the e-bike revolution and cycling in general will find it a worthwhile read. In the chapters ahead, we will explore the health benefits of cycling, including e-bikes. You will learn how to select an e-bike, maintain it, protect it, and ride it more safely. You will hear from e-bike industry leaders and cycling trendsetters, and from senior-adult cyclists who have embraced the e-bike life with enthusiasm. 👓

Acknowledgements

Before we launch into this adventure together, I want to first thank my wife, Kathy, who has tolerated hours of solitude as I labored on this book at home over the past several months. She's also my first-line editor and proofreader, and a very good one at that.

I also want to thank Dee Dee Evans, of The Write Stuff Editing Services, who provided invaluable book-editing expertise. Fellow author Rebecca Warner generously shared her publishing advice with me, for which I am deeply grateful. Thanks too to Cristina Miller, graphic designer extraordinaire with Nine31 Creative, for her help with the cover design, layout, and branding of this venture.

I interviewed numerous industry leaders for this book and appreciate their time and patience with me. My special thanks go to Jason Kraft, CEO of Electric Bike Technologies; Court Rye, founder of ElectricBikeReview.com; and Don DiCostanzo, co-founder and CEO of Pedego Electric Bikes.

Some of my most enjoyable research was the many hours spent talking with fellow e-bike cyclists, who shared their inspiring stories of how electric bikes have strengthened their health, added adventure to their retirement years, and generally improved their happiness and quality of life. If you are not yet excited about e-bikes and what they can do for you, you will be after reading their profiles, found at the end of each chapter.

If you enjoy this book and want to keep up with the latest news and stories about e-bikes and the e-bike lifestyle, please visit my blog at **ThisEBikeLife.com**. I also author a second blog on more general retirement-living trends at **ThisRetirementLife.com**.

Thanks for taking time to download or purchase this book. My hope is that after reading it your childhood love affair with bikes will be rekindled and that cycling will add better health, adventure, and fun to your senior years ahead. If you enjoy it, tell friends and encourage them to buy and read it too. Maybe they will become your new e-bike riding partners. 👓

Introduction

When Keith Pegg was in his mid-60s and ready to retire, he realized he had gained too much weight and wasn't getting enough exercise. Now 71, Keith credits riding his electric-powered bicycle for helping him get in better shape.

"I think the e-bike has saved my life. As long as I can ride, I will." Keith Pegg, 71, credits riding his electric-powered bicycle for helping him get in better shape.

"I started at 330 pounds and had a few health problems," Keith said. "I am now down to 270 pounds. I still take some medications but my health is much better. I have lost 60 pounds — 90 percent because of my bike."

Despite the famously rainy weather where he lives in Ocean Shores, Washington, Keith said he rides about 270 days a year, averaging 8 to 12 miles per ride. He's put more than 12,000 miles on his electric bike.

"I think the e-bike has saved my life. As long as I can ride, I will."

If you're approaching retirement age or already there, you likely can relate to Keith. You're not as young as you used to be, but you still want to feel strong and healthy. You long for something new that will give you a sense of enthusiasm and adventure during this chapter of life. You're searching for an activity that will not only help you feel better but that you will look forward to doing, something fun that will put a smile on your face every single time.

If that describes you, this book can help you achieve these objectives. It will introduce you to the amazing world of e-bikes, a revolutionary new product that is transforming the lives of people around the globe, and especially senior adults.

E-bikes really can put the FUN back into cycling (and life) at any age. This book will show you how. Whether you are just thinking about buying your first e-bike and want to learn more, or whether you are an experienced e-bike rider who wants to delve deeper, this book will both inform and inspire you.

What You Will Learn

Here is what you can look forward to when reading *E-bikes - Putting the fun Back Into Cycling (and Life) at any age:*

- Gain a better understanding of e-bikes, including their history, uses, and regulation.

- Explore the life-changing health and exercise benefits of cycling, and why riding an e-bike is still extremely beneficial for you despite the power assist.

- Become a better-informed consumer when buying an e-bike, learning what features to look for, and the pros and cons of buying through a local dealer versus online.

- Learn important safety and riding tips that can keep you from becoming a cycling accident statistic.

- Understand how to properly maintain your new e-bike and protect it from theft and other risks.

As an added bonus, when reading this book you will learn about many senior-adult, real-life e-bike enthusiasts, from all walks of life, who tell their personal stories of how electric bikes have changed their lives for the better.

About the Author

Dave Hogan, the author and your companion for this journey, is delighted to be here with you! Enjoy the ride!

The author of this book, Dave Hogan, is a fellow Baby Boomer, a life-long cyclist, and an e-bike enthusiast. Through his popular blog, This Retirement Life, the author has been helping inform senior adults about how to better enjoy this special stage of life. His newest blog, This E-Bike Life, helps readers with tips and stories about how to get the most from their e-bike experience.

Like many Baby Boomer children, Dave's love for cycling goes back to childhood. It was a bike that first gave him independence, a chance to explore the world around him, and the unforgettable rush of the wind in your face as you ride your two-wheel wonder machine down the street. When Dave got married, he and his wife, Kathy, gave each other matching bikes as wedding gifts and rode them for many years.

Similar to many of you who have already experienced your first ride on an e-bike, Dave's enthusiasm for cycling rose to a new high a few years ago when he acquired his first electric-powered bicycle. Life hasn't been the same since. Dave credits his e-bike not only for weight loss and overall better health, but for expanding his travel and exploration opportunities and giving him something fun and exciting to look forward to each day.

Why Read This Book?

The author of this book, *E-bikes - Putting the fun Back Into Cycling (and Life) at any age,* is one of the growing legion of Baby Boomer e-bike addicts. Throughout this book, Dave will share what he's learned with you in hopes that your health and life also will be enriched through learning more about the e-bike phenomenon.

But fair warning, you just might become an e-bike addict like Dave!

While it sounds like a worn cliche to say so, **reading this book truly can change your life.** Riding an e-bike will add a new dimension to your senior years, improve your health, and make you feel younger. We hope you enjoy every page of this book and want to tell your friends about it too.

Soon, you too will be smiling like never before and will have your own e-bike story to share. 👓

CHAPTER 1

Welcome to the E-Bike Revolution

"You can't buy happiness, but you can buy a bike, and that's pretty close."

– *Unknown*

"This e-bike changed my life. I'm 63 years old with a bad heart and pacemaker and autonomic dysfunction. I thought my fun bike riding days were over. I have a new lease on life. I am loving it!"

– *A senior cyclist on Facebook*

Want to see a senior adult's face light up with a big grin? Ask her about her grandchildren. Or ask him about his e-bike.

Electric-powered bicycles have created a buzz among seniors unlike anything else. It's a euphoria that is hard to describe to those who have not yet tried riding an e-bike. But those who own them will be more than happy to share their stories with you. Don't be surprised if they whip out their phones to share cycling photos with you, just like proud grandparents do when asked about their grandchildren.

Few products have revolutionized senior living in recent years more than electric bikes. Riding e-bikes has improved the physical and mental health of thousands of older adults, opened up new possibilities for travel and adventure, and reignited the joy of bicycling that so many of us experienced as children.

When the conversation with a Baby Boomer turns to their experience with an e-bike, you will hear phrases like these over and over again:

"Life changing."

"I feel like a kid again."

It's true. E-bikes really can bring the FUN back to cycling (and life) again, no matter what your age.

Baby Boomers Embrace E-Bikes

"We are the forever-young generation," said Don DiCostanzo, co-founder and CEO of Pedego Electric Bikes, the largest retailer of e-bikes in the United States. "Yes, we're turning into seniors, but we're begging, borrowing, and stealing to do everything we can to stay as young as we can, and riding an e-bike is part of that."

A senior himself, DiCostanzo (left) knows first hand the benefits of riding an electric bike.

"I'm 63 years old and have lost 20 pounds. I'm in the best physical shape I've ever been in my life. I have unbelievable balance, even though I was a clumsy person my whole life. Today, I'm not clumsy at all. My reaction time has improved. When you're riding a bike, you're constantly balancing. All of the things in your physiology that are designed to help you with balance are being played every second you are on the bike."

You can learn more about DiCostanzo and Pedego's success by reading his Rider Profile at the end of Chapter 6. Each chapter of this book will end with a profile of a senior cyclist who will inspire you to take up e-bike cycling if you haven't done so yet or ride more often and creatively if you already own an e-bike.

E-Bike Sales Soar Worldwide

In 2020, Americans bought new e-bikes at the rate of about one every 52 seconds. Adult bike sales are growing worldwide, with e-bikes leading the way. In 2020, e-bike sales in the U.S. grew 145 percent over 2019, more than double the growth rate of other bikes, according to data from the NPD Group, an American marketing research firm.

More than one million e-bikes are expected to be sold in the U.S. in 2021, smashing all previous records, according to Ed Benjamin, chairman of the Light Electric Vehicle Association (LEVA). He believes sales will continue to soar, hitting three million per year in the U.S. within the next few years.

"The United States tends to make changes slowly until a tipping point is reached. And then, change can be startlingly fast," said Benjamin, a known expert on electric bikes, in a report posted by ElectricBikeReport.com. "That tipping point has occurred with electric bikes in the last two years. We are on our way to becoming the most profitable and largest Western market for electric bikes."

Much the same is happening in Europe and elsewhere. E-bike sales are setting new records in international markets as diverse as Australia, Japan, and Israel. The United Kingdom's Bicycle Association reports that 160,000 e-bikes were sold there in 2020, far outpacing sales of electric cars. Electric bike sales across Europe now account for 17 percent of all bike sales and that number is growing rapidly. Industry sources predict that annual e-bike sales in the European Union will grow from their current (2020) level of 3.7 million to 17 million per year by 2030, by that point accounting for more than half of all new bike sales.

Compared to the U.S. and Canada, bicycles are a more accepted form of transportation in much of Europe and Asia. They are used for commuting to work and running errands, not just for recreation. In the Netherlands, an estimated 78 percent of the population rides a bike at least once each month. Bike usage varies by country in the EU, but it is growing nearly everywhere. By the year 2030, it is estimated that new-bike sales each year in Europe will be double the number of annual new-car sales.

E-bikes, often referred to in Europe as "pedelecs" (short for "pedal electric bikes"), are more common there than in North America. A survey sponsored by Shimano, a bike components manufacturer, found that nearly one-in-four Europeans (24 percent) either already own an e-bike or plan to buy or use one soon.

China is by far the largest market for electric bikes. Chinese consumers now own more than 300 million e-bikes. For comparison, that's nearly equal to one e-bike for every man, woman, and child in the United States. Not surprisingly, China is also the largest manufacturer and exporter of e-bikes.

Regardless of which brand of e-bike you purchase, it is most likely manufactured in China or Taiwan, or at least assembled in North America using frames, motors and other components from China or Taiwan. That's not to say Europe doesn't have a well-established and respected bicycle industry (it does), or that more U.S. and Canadian e-bike manufacturers are emerging, but the overall market is still dominated by China and Taiwan.

In North America, the UK, Japan, and other markets, senior adults buy a disproportionately large percentage of e-bikes. Younger buyers are beginning to adopt e-bikes too but for different purposes, such as commuting to work, carrying children on errands, making urban business deliveries, and to enhance traditional cycling sports like road biking and mountain biking. While the COVID pandemic may explain some of the unusually strong sales during 2020-2021, it is clear that deeper, longer-term trends are in play that favor the greater use of bicycles and in particular electric-powered bikes.

Why Cycling Is Booming

Bicycle sales and usage among adults are booming, and these trends go well beyond the short-term bump up in sales in 2020-2021 from the COVID virus pandemic. The introduction of e-bikes may be the most important factor spurring this long-term growth in cycling, especially among senior adults, but it's not the whole story. Before I go into a deeper discussion about e-bikes, let's look at some other reasons why cycling is booming:

Bike riding is good for you. More people today are looking for ways to exercise and stay healthy. This is especially true of senior adults, who understand the benefits of exercise for both physical and mental health. They want to remain independent and healthy for as many years as possible. As we will explore in more detail in Chapter 4, **cycling is a simple and effective form of exercise that most people can enjoy regardless of age. You don't have to be an athlete to ride a bike.** When you read the Rider Profiles at the end of each chapter, you will be inspired by stories about seniors who have improved their health through cycling.

Bikes are good for the environment. Bicycles are human-powered, with no gas motors to spew pollutants into the air. They are one of the most energy-efficient forms of transportation. Every errand run and every job commute made by bike instead of a car or truck helps the environment. According to data reported by Juiced Bikes, every four-mile trip made by e-bike instead of by car keeps 15 pounds of pollutants from entering the air. **While a car puts 271 grams of harmful carbon monoxide (CO) emissions into the air for every kilometer traveled, an e-bike only generates 21 to 22 grams.**

In nations around the world, bikes are increasingly being viewed as a serious means of transportation that should be encouraged through "green" legislation, infrastructure spending, and transportation policy. Some countries are offering incentives or tax credits for people who purchase e-bikes. Many nations are phasing out the sale of new gas- and diesel-powered vehicles and encouraging the sale of electric vehicles of all types — cars, trucks, and bicycles. E-bikes will play an important role in the future of transportation on our planet, especially in larger urban markets.

Better bike infrastructure is making cycling safer and more convenient. Thousands of miles of new, dedicated trails for pedestrians and cyclists built in recent years now make it possible for bicyclists in some cities to largely avoid riding in the roads with cars. Other cities have designated bike lanes and improved signage to encourage more and safer bike usage. Long-distance cycling highways are emerging, such as the EuroVelo network in Europe. Across Europe and North America, longer trails are making possible safer bike travel between states or countries. **Giving cyclists a safer place to ride is key to increasing cycling ridership.** It's a perfect example of the old saying borrowed from another sport: "build it and they will come."

Cycling is fun! Whether riding around the neighborhood or across the continent, cycling is just plain fun. **There's something special about the rush of air and the motion of riding a bike that makes a person feel more alive and energized.** Seniors are finding new ways to enjoy their bikes that combine their interests in travel, adventure, and cycling. Bike tourism and bike touring have emerged as popular travel and vacation options. Many cycling tour packages target the growing senior-adult market. There's no better way to explore a new place slowly and close up than while riding a bike.

Is an E-Bike Right for You?

If you are the typical Baby Boomer, you don't have the strength or stamina you had 30 years ago. Your joints may hurt. You may have breathing issues. Your muscle strength has slowly declined. Those hills that were challenging even at age 30 are now all but impossible to climb on a bicycle at age 60-plus. All of these factors help explain why low-speed electric bikes are so well suited for most senior adults. **An e-bike helps you stay in the game and allows you to remain active, both physically and socially.** An e-bike improves your fitness level, keeps alive your sense of adventure, and enhances your enjoyment of the outdoors. You can achieve these results even if failing health and old age restrict your other sports and fitness opportunities.

That doesn't mean, however, that an e-bike is the best solution for every senior cyclist. Those seniors who are not likely to want an e-bike may include the following:

Super fit senior warriors. There are many seniors who are exceptionally fit and have ridden bikes for exercise for decades. Perhaps they've competed in cycling races or triathlons. They aren't ready to transition to an e-bike, preferring the greater physical challenge of a traditional bike. If you are one of these two-wheel senior road warriors, by all means, keep wearing those spandex biker outfits and riding your lightweight road bikes for as long as you can. We salute you! You are likely among the most-fit seniors on the planet. At the same time, please don't stand in judgment of your peers who choose to ride e-bikes. We're not all as fit or capable as you.

Seniors who don't know how to ride a bike or have poor balance. At the other far end of the spectrum, if you never mastered the art of riding a bike as a child or young adult, or have serious balance and coordination issues, then you may be safer sticking with walking, hiking, swimming, and other physical activities. Riding an e-bike is a lot more fun than riding a traditional bike, but it's still a bicycle. The same dynamics of balancing and coordinating are at play. **If this describes you but you are still interested in trying an e-bike, go to a bike shop and test ride one or more e-bike models before buying.** Try different sizes and types of e-bikes. Some are easier to ride than others. You can also rent e-bikes by the hour or the day, if you wish to test your skills. If you are in this category, don't buy until you are sure you can safely ride an e-bike. Most people can, but not everyone.

Even if you are not a good candidate for a two-wheel e-bike due to balance issues or other health concerns, you don't have to miss out on the fun (and health benefits) of cycling. **You may still enjoy the e-bike's close cousin, the electric tricycle.** Since a trike has three wheels, balance is no longer a factor. Adult-size e-trikes come in a variety of styles and configurations. Thanks to e-trikes, many seniors who are no longer capable or comfortable riding a two-wheel bike can now enjoy the same outdoor exercise, mobility, social benefits, and beautiful bike trails along with everyone else. (I will discuss electric trikes later in Chapter 8.)

The occasional or short-distance bike rider. A third group of seniors who may not be as keenly interested in e-bikes is those who ride only within their neighborhood or on very short errands and live on flat terrain with paved trails, bike lanes, or low-traffic roads. You may find a traditional bike easy enough to ride without incurring the expense of transitioning to an e-bike. You may feel you get all of the exercise you want from your traditional bike.

To this final group, if you're happy with your traditional bike, that's great. Riding ANY bicycle is better than riding none at all. At the same time, please consider the fact that you may be missing out on a world of fun by restricting your cycling experience to only your neighborhood. With thousands of miles of bike trails and a growing number of bike-touring options, an e-bike can open up amazing opportunities for inspiring travel adventures that you will likely never know on your traditional bike. E-bikes can also be a surprisingly practical transportation alternative for running errands or commuting to a job.

You will see what I mean when you read the Rider Profiles scattered throughout this book. You will be inspired by these e-bike cyclists' stories of discovery and adventure. You just might be motivated enough to join the e-bike revolution.

On the next page, you will read the first Rider Profile, about Les and Linda Tocknell, a senior couple who enjoy cycling with their e-bikes in the English countryside where they live — and even exploring Europe by bike. 👓

Les and Linda Tocknell

Conquering England's Hills With E-Bikes

"The difference this (e-bikes) has made has been astonishing."

- Les Tocknell

"When we get back from a hilly 30+ miles we are tired, but not exhausted, which means we can confidently ride the next day...If that's cheating, we're happy cheats!" Les and Linda Tocknell, UK

Since UK couple Les and Linda Tocknell first bought e-bikes about five years ago, they've heard the occasional complaint that riding an e-bike is "cheating" and not really exercising.

They know better.

"When we get back from a hilly 30+ miles we are tired, but not exhausted, which means we can confidently ride the next day without excessive fatigue," Les said. "Apparently some people think e-bikes are cheating. If that's cheating, we're happy cheats!"

Les, 70, and Linda, 67, live in Ross on Wye, a market town in Herefordshire, in the UK. In the Wye Valley and the Forest of Dean where they ride their e-bikes, the countryside is beautiful but hilly, making cycling more challenging.

"There are not many flat bits. It's either up or down," Les said.

They first discovered e-bikes while on a bike tour in 2016 in the Czech Republic. Les said they noticed older people using e-bikes in their daily activities. The mountains on this tour were daunting, so they started doing research into e-bikes.

The "flame was lit" as Les put it, and it wasn't long before both of them bought e-bikes. Linda purchased a Cube Tour Pro with step-through frame design and Les bought a Scott E-Sub Evo.

"The difference this (e-bike) has made has been astonishing. Hills and mountains are now not a problem," Les said. "We may have done some touring as we got older but my suspicion is that we wouldn't have. The e-bikes certainly make a difference that is significant and defining."

Around home and in the UK, Les and Linda often bike with good friends Steve and Jan. Cycling together has been much more enjoyable since purchasing the e-bikes.

"Our foursome takes on some challenging hills with no moans and groans," Les said. "In fact, very often, there are exclamations of pleasure as the views open up."

Encouraged by their e-bikes, Les and Linda have taken several more adventurous cycling holidays and tours. They enjoyed a holiday in England's Peak District where they took on challenging climbs that Les says they would not have attempted without the e-bikes. Les and Steve also cycled the Gospel Pass, considered the highest road in Wales.

The couple have returned twice to cycle in the Czech Republic and have cycled through parts of Germany. Their routes have included steep mountains, remote forests, and other challenging terrain. While pleased with their bikes' performance through all these trips, they do caution other senior adults to be aware that e-bikes are heavy, so lifting them onto trains and other public transport is not always easy.

Les and Linda are sold on the benefits of e-bikes, especially for senior adults.

"We would never have experienced all this without the e-bikes," Les said. "We are confident our e-bike adventures will carry on for some time to come."

CHAPTER 2

Why Seniors Are Rushing to Buy E-Bikes

"You might enjoy an electric bike if you are the kind of person who would enjoy feeling 30 years younger. Otherwise, forget about it."

– A senior cyclist on Facebook

"I'm 73 years old with an incurable arthritic disease and I just logged 1,000 miles in under five months (on an e-bike)."

– A senior cyclist on Facebook

Seniors Praise Their E-Bikes

It's not hyperbole to say that e-bikes are literally life-changing for many seniors. Nor is it uncommon to hear tales from seniors about how e-bikes have improved their physical or emotional health and brought new fun and adventure to their lives.

On Facebook group pages devoted to bicycling, senior cycling enthusiasts often talk about the positive impact e-bikes have had on their lives.

A senior rider from Pretoria, South Africa, recently noted:

"I have serious osteoarthritis of the hips and knees. I have just had my first full hip replacement. If not for my e-bike, I wouldn't be having fun with my friends."

In another Facebook post, a senior cyclist in Ottawa, Ontario in Canada made this observation:

"I bought mine (e-bike) to keep active. After three and a half years, I can't believe all the wonderful touring and exploring the e-bike has taken me to. I have a bad hip and some days can barely walk, but I ride my e-bike every single day, rain or shine, 30 to 80 kilometers (18.6 to 49.7 miles). Talk about feeling like a kid again!"

A senior cyclist in California shared this comment:

"I've ridden my e-bike more in the past three months than I rode my regular bike in the past 10 years."

Understanding Electric Bikes

So what exactly is an e-bike, and what makes it so ideally suited for senior adults?

First and foremost, it's important to note that *in terms of design and purpose, an electric bike is still a bicycle.* While a few e-bikes mimic the design features of a moped or motorcycle, for the most part when you see an e-bike it will look like any other bicycle. The most visible sign of an e-bike is the large battery mounted somewhere on the frame or on the rear luggage rack. Some models even do a good job of concealing the battery for a more sleek and stealth e-bike look. E-bikes also have a motor mounted on either one of the wheels or between the pedals and a controller (LED display) mounted on the handlebars. Otherwise, they simply look like any other bicycle.

Most nations or states define an e-bike (called a "pedelec" in Europe) as a type of bicycle, not as a motorized vehicle requiring registration. To be an e-bike, it must have pedals and be propelled forward solely or primarily by human power, just like any other bicycle. It is distinctly different from a scooter, moped, or motorcycle.

To help us define terms, let's look at how the U.S. government defines an e-bike.

The U.S. Consumer Products Safety Act defines a "low speed electric bicycle" as "a two-or three-wheeled vehicle with fully operable pedals and an electric motor of less than 750 watts, whose maximum speed on a paved level surface, when powered solely by such a motor while ridden by an operator who weighs 170 pounds, is less than 20 mph."

Most U.S. states have followed the federal example in defining e-bikes as bicycles and not as motor vehicles. The U.S. Department of the Interior, in a 2019 memorandum, cited the federal definition and concluded that electric bikes have equal access as traditional bikes to national parks and other federal public lands managed by the Bureau of Land Management, Fish and Wildlife Service, and the Bureau of Reclamation.

Making matters more confusing, however, is the fact that each national park's leadership can set its own rules, so before riding an electric bike in a national park, you will need to research their regulations. Most will allow at least Class 1 e-bikes, which I will explain below. Local jurisdictions, such as towns and cities, which often control bike trails in their area, also can set policies that are more restrictive than the federal standard.

The European Union, comprised of 27 nations, has its own standards for electric-powered bicycles. In the EU, an e-bike is restricted to a maximum speed of 25 km/h (15.5 mph), is not equipped with a throttle, and has a smaller electric motor not to exceed 250 watts versus the 750 watt U.S. maximum size. These are pedal-assisted bikes only, meaning if you are not pedaling, there is no power. In practical terms, this means pedelecs in the EU do not have throttles as is common on e-bikes sold in North America.

The EU also allows for a higher-powered version of electric bicycles, called speed pedelecs, or s-pedelecs, but in most of Europe these bikes require licensing like a moped or scooter and may not legally be ridden on bike paths or cycleways. Officially, only these higher-powered cycles in Europe are referred to as "e-bikes." In this book, we will follow the North American practice of referring to all of these classifications of bicycles as "e-bikes." Even though they require insurance and licensing, s-pedelecs are nevertheless growing in popularity in some parts of Europe.

The United Kingdom generally follows the same rules as the European Union when it comes to e-bike classification.

Canadian regulations fall between the U.S. and EU. In Canada, e-bikes are restricted to no more than 500 watts of power and cannot exceed speeds of 32 km/h (20 mph). Throttles are allowed.

In simplest terms, **consumers may distinguish e-bikes from traditional bicycles as bicycles that have electric motors powered by an on-board, rechargeable electric battery.** E-bikes are regulated to remain low-speed vehicles, with top-end speeds similar to traditional bikes.

E-Bike Classifications

Beyond these basic definitions, e-bikes in the U.S. are further identified by a three-tier classification system adopted on a state-by-state basis as described below. This classification was developed by PeopleForBikes, a national bicycle advocacy group and bicycle industry trade association. Thanks to PeopleForBikes' tireless advocacy, more than two-thirds of U.S. states have adopted this classification system.

CLASS 2
750W
20MPH

Bike manufacturers or retailers should provide you with a classification sticker like the one shown in this photo. Display it on your bike in case authorities question you about your e-bike. Some local jurisdictions, parks, and bike trails prohibit Class 3 e-bikes, while some only allow Class 1 e-bikes. Depending on where you live, this could be a factor in which e-bike you choose to purchase.

The classifications of electric bikes, taken from the PeopleForBikes website, are as follows:

⚙ *"Class 1 electric bicycle" shall mean an electric bicycle equipped with a motor that provides assistance only when the rider is pedaling, and that ceases to provide assistance when the bicycle reaches the speed of 20 miles per hour.*

⚙ *"Class 2 electric bicycle" shall mean an electric bicycle equipped with a motor that may be used exclusively to propel the bicycle, and that is not capable of providing assistance when the bicycle reaches the speed of 20 miles per hour.*

⚙ *"Class 3 electric bicycle" shall mean an electric bicycle equipped with a motor that provides assistance only when the rider is pedaling, and that ceases to provide assistance when the bicycle reaches the speed of 28 miles per hour, and is equipped with a speedometer.*

While this classification system may sound confusing, it has helped to standardize policies among the U.S. states. The Class 2 definition refers to e-bikes with a throttle, similar to a throttle on a motorcycle. A throttle allows the rider to power the e-bike forward without pedaling. I will discuss the pros and cons of throttles in more detail in Chapter 6.

The Class 3 definition does not mention a throttle, but in the North American marketplace many e-bikes are sold with both pedal assist and a throttle and are capable of speeds up to 28 mph. These e-bikes are classified as Class 3 e-bikes.

Class 3 e-bikes are problematic in some jurisdictions because of their higher top speed, which exceeds the U.S. federal limit of 20 mph. In the eyes of policymakers in these jurisdictions, the fact that these bikes also have throttles makes matters even worse. In most national parks in the U.S., for instance, a Class 3 e-bike would be classified as a motor vehicle, not a bicycle, and not permitted on trails or other areas where traditional bikes and Class 1 and Class 2 e-bikes are allowed.

In practice, few parks or trails are going to stop e-bike cyclists who are riding at normal speeds and not causing a disturbance. Even if you own a Class 3 e-bike, if you practice good trail etiquette and obey speed limits, odds are no one is going to care about your bike's classification. Even so, you are accepting a higher level of liability risk by riding an illegal e-bike on these trails. If you were to cause an accident and another cyclist or pedestrian were injured, you can be sure their attorney would zero in on the fact that you were riding an illegal vehicle. If you own a Class 3 e-bike, a better solution is to see if it can be temporarily or permanently reset to the Class 2 speed restriction. This is possible with many e-bikes. Ask your local bike shop or the manufacturer for instructions.

Which Class of E-Bike Should You Buy?

For the average, recreation-focused senior adult to whom this book is speaking most directly, buying a Class 1 or Class 2 e-bike makes the most sense. Younger people using their e-bikes to commute to work in city traffic may want the higher speed of a Class 3 e-bike, but that is not how most of us Baby Boomers are using our bikes. We are cycling for fun and exercise and do not need the extra speed of a Class 3 e-bike. To the contrary, buying an e-bike that will travel up to 28 mph with a throttle or pedal assist increases your risk of serious injury or death in the event of a cycling accident. Buying a Class 3 e-bike also means you may frequently be riding illegally and subjecting yourself to greater liability if you ride your e-bike on multi-purpose paths and park trails, as described in the paragraph above. You will do well to steer clear of Class 3 e-bikes, or ask the dealer if he can reset the bike as a Class 2 and change its sticker.

Choosing between a Class 1 or Class 2 e-bike comes down to whether or not you want a throttle. Class 1 e-bikes do not have throttles and are more akin to Europe's pedelecs. Class 2 e-bikes have throttles. I will talk more about the pros and cons of throttles later in this book. For now, be aware that some U.S. trails only allow Class 1 e-bikes. I personally like having a throttle and think these restrictions are unfortunate and unnecessary. Nevertheless, before buying a new e-bike you may want to inquire with your local and state trail systems where you are most likely to ride to see what is considered legal there.

Alternatively, you can purchase a Class 2 e-bike that allows you to easily turn off or disable the throttle. This is how I deal with the throttle issue. I own a Class 2 e-bike on which the throttle can be quickly disabled or even removed, effectively making it a Class 1 e-bike when necessary.

E-Bikes: Ideally Suited for Senior Adults

As you can see from the stories of senior-adult cyclists cited earlier in this chapter, e-bikes are indeed revolutionary for seniors. The extra power of the electric motor is like magic. It helps our aging bodies keep pedaling ahead — and enjoying every mile of it. With an e-bike, you are likely to ride farther and more often. An e-bike may enable you to keep pace and enjoy riding again with a more physically fit spouse or partner — or with your children and grandchildren. No longer will your bicycle just sit in the garage gathering dust. You will want to ride it as often as possible. You will challenge yourself to explore new trails, join cycling groups, take a bike tour or vacation — all things you might never have attempted as a senior adult with a traditional bike.

In future chapters, I will discuss the health and recreational benefits of riding an electric bike and will share what you need to know before buying one. I will give you tips on how to ride safely, how to maintain your bike, and what accessories you may need. In short, I will show you how to put the FUN back into cycling (and life) at any age!

Before going to the next chapter, be sure to read the Rider Profile on the next page about Jack and Jan Gee, a senior couple who have combined their love of travel, RVs, and e-bikes to make their retirement years even more enjoyable. 👓

RIDER PROFILE

Jack and Jan Gee

Combining Their Love of RVs and E-Bikes

"It (e-bike) has got me to be a bicyclist. I want to stay healthy and to keep moving."

- Jack Gee

Jack Gee, 71, and his wife Jan are on their second set of e-bikes and take them with them wherever they travel with their RV.

Jack and Jan Gee used to ride regular bicycles, but all it took was one test ride on an e-bike to convince them to make the switch.

"For me, bike riding on a regular bike, I enjoyed it but wasn't really avid about it," Jack said. "Then I started reading about e-bikes and went to a bike shop. He let me take one out and demo it around the building. I went around the parking lot about three times and I was hooked. That's all it took."

Now, three years later, Jack, 71, and his wife Jan are on their second set of e-bikes (Ride1Up brand) and take them with them wherever they travel with their RV. They recently completed a six-week biking vacation in Alabama and have also ridden trails in Mississippi and Florida, as well as their home state of Michigan.

Describing themselves as active seniors, Jan said she even rides almost daily during Michigan's harsh winters, in addition to running. She will ride in the snow, but not ice.

"I won't go out on the ice. That's scary," Jan said.

For this retired couple, e-bikes play an important role in keeping them healthy. "It's got me to be a bicyclist," Jack said. "I want to stay healthy and to keep moving."

Exercise is important to Jack and Jan, and their e-bikes allow them to get plenty of it.

"I like it because you can work as hard as you want," Jack said. "We don't ever just cruise around without pedaling. We keep the PAS (pedal assist setting) low and the gearing high and just ride that way."

Like most retired seniors, Jack and Jan try to pack a lot of activities into their busy days. E-bikes help them make more efficient use of their time.

"What the e-bike has done is I really love riding the bike because you can go farther and faster," Jack said. "When I bike, I don't want to spend a half day biking because I have too many other interests. With an e-bike, it affords me the ability to go 20 miles in just over an hour and be done." 👓

Cycling's Colorful Past and Promising Future; How Bikes Have Helped Push Societal Change

"Whoever invented the bicycle deserves the thanks of humanity."
– Lord Charles Beresford

"The discovery and progressive improvement of the bicycle is of more importance to mankind than all the victories and defeats of Napoleon, with the First and Second Punic Wars ... thrown in."
– New York Post editorial, 1896

There are far more bicycles on the planet than automobiles. Today, the world has more than one billion bicycles. They are widely used throughout most of the world, either for pleasure or more commonly as an affordable means of transportation.

Bicycles play an important role in the world today, but they also have had a colorful and fascinating history. To more fully appreciate your pursuit of bicycling, it helps to gain an appreciation for this history. Perhaps surprisingly, even electric bikes have a much longer history than you might expect.

In this chapter, I will look at both the history of electric bikes and how they are reshaping the future of cycling and society. The introduction of e-bikes is far more significant and impactful to our future world than many realize.

Karl von Drais, a German, is credited as the father of the bicycle for his 1817 invention of the first two-wheel, steerable vehicle (shown in the rendering at left). It had no pedals, leading to one of its nicknames as "the running machine." It also was referred to as a "velocipede" or "hobby horse."

Not only are there far more bicycles on the planet than automobiles, but bikes also have a longer history. The predecessors of today's bikes originated in Europe, about two hundred years ago. These early contraptions had odd-size wheels and no pedals, as inventors struggled to find the right design.

In the 1860s, several French inventors developed the first bikes with pedals and the term "bicycle" first came into use. A decade later, the "penny farthing" or "high wheeler" created the first boom in bike sales. This unusual design is remembered for its oversized front tire. Bicycle clubs and racing began to spring up around this time. Still, bikes were not yet ready for the masses. The penny farthing required athletic skill to ride, toppled easily, and wasn't practical for everyday use.

The Safety Bicycle and the 1890s Bike Boom

The design of the modern bicycle came into being in 1885 when Englishman John Kemp Starley developed the "safety bicycle," which featured two equal-size wheels and a chain drive. The design is not that different from today's bikes.

Starley's safety bike, shown here, was the first bike that the average person could enjoy riding. Cycling was no longer an oddity or limited only to athletes. Thanks to the safety bike, older people and women enjoyed cycling alongside younger men. "Senior cycling" became a thing. One cycling club in New York limited members to men age 60 and over.

It's interesting to note that at this point in history it was rare for a child to own a bicycle. Cycling was considered a sport for adults. Plus, bicycles were too rare and expensive for children.

The safety bike led to an unprecedented boom in bike sales in the 1890s. Bicycling became a cultural phenomenon. By mid-decade, more than 300 manufacturers in the United States were producing bicycles. One of the largest factories ran day and night, turning out a new bike every minute. Interestingly, that is about the same production rate as the number of e-bikes sold in the U.S. in 2020, although the vast majority of them came from Asian factories.

Among the manufacturers and retailers of bikes during the 1890s were two brothers, Wilbur and Orville Wright. They opened a bike shop in 1892 in Dayton, Ohio. It was from their bike business that the Wright Brothers earned the money to pursue their other more far-fetched dream of building a flying machine. Today, Orville and Wilbur are remembered as the first ones to successfully fly a powered aircraft, but their roots were in the bicycle business.

You can still visit a replica of the Wright Brothers' bike shop at the Wright Brothers National Museum in Dayton's Carillon Historical Park. The actual building that housed the Wright Cycle Shop has been relocated to Dearborn, Michigan, and is on display at The Henry Ford Museum in Greenfield Village.

Bicycling's Impact on Highways, Women's Rights and Tourism

The 1890s bike boom led to many societal changes as well. Having not lived in that time, it may be hard for most of us today to understand the gushingly favorable comments and extreme enthusiasm that cycling generated during that time period. Even the U.S. Census Bureau commented in a report that "Few articles ever used by man have ever created so great a revolution in social conditions."

Among the changes with lasting consequences for the nation was the start of modern road construction and highways. In a time of horse and buggies and before the popularity of motorized vehicles, in the 1890s roads in America were dismal, marked by mud and deep ruts. Cycling groups such as the League of American Wheelmen, now the League of American Bicyclists, pushed for better roads, highways, and road directional signage.

Cycling was popular with both men and women. Biking contributed to the women's movement by giving women greater freedom of movement and independence. Riding bicycles even led to shorter skirts for women. This was at a time when women had not yet won the right to vote in the U.S., Canada, and most of Europe.

The 1890s bike boom contributed to the women's movement by giving women greater freedom of movement and independence.

As a result, U.S. pioneering women's rights advocate Susan B. Anthony said this about the role of bicycles:

"The bicycle has done more for the emancipation of women than anything else in the world."

Ann Strong, a journalist, wrote in 1895:

"The bicycle is just as good company as most husbands and, when it gets old and shabby, a woman can dispose of it and get a new one without shocking the entire community."

Thanks to bicycles, the common man could ride beyond his own town to explore the countryside and other cities. **Biking's popularity led to a significant boom in travel and tourism.** The first dedicated bike trails began to appear around this time, although most were later abandoned. Organized bike tours into the countryside flourished.

Bicycle racing as a spectator sport also blossomed during the 1890s. As a professional sport, cycle racing actually pre-dates both basketball and baseball. More than 100 velodromes and other cycling tracks operated in the U.S. alone in the 1890s; one of the more famous velodromes was in the original Madison Square Garden in New York City.

Sadly, the 1890s biking boom was short-lived. The new century ushered in the automobile, which caught the public's fancy. New passenger trains also offered a more convenient way to travel beyond one's hometown. The bicycle lost its luster and began gathering dust in garages and backyards.

Baby Boomers Generate the 1970s Bike Boom

The Baby Boom generation was largely responsible for the next big surge in the popularity of bicycles. Many of us grew up riding our Schwinn, Huffy, or Murray children's bikes. Bicycles played a significant role in our childhood. Our bikes gave us freedom to roam. The feeling of wind in our face as we rode was addictive.

In the 1970s, as most of us were coming into adulthood, society became more concerned about fitness and exercise. Gas prices soared, making car travel more expensive. We Baby Boomers turned back to bicycles, but this time we traded the small bikes with banana seats for adult-size bikes with 10-speed gears, thin tires, and turned-down handlebars wrapped with tape.

My wife and I were part of that 1970s bike craze. We bought matching red Raleigh bikes for each other as wedding gifts and rode them for many years. When I went to graduate school and my wife got a job at the university, we rode to campus each day on our bikes, weather permitting. When our first child came along, we bought a rear child's seat for her and kept riding.

Probably like many of you from that generation who are reading this book, somewhere along the way the demands of careers and rearing children pushed our bikes to the garage. For too many of us, our bikes got only occasional use during much of our adult life. It wasn't until the past decade that we have begun to rediscover the joys and benefits of cycling. We turned back to cycling for many reasons, including our renewed interest in staying fit and healthy and the growing popularity of appealing and safe bike trails.

For my wife and me, and I suspect for many of you, the most significant development that brought us back to our bikes was the introduction of the e-bike. At last, cycling is fun again. Hills and overpasses are no longer a struggle, even with our older, tired joints and other health issues. We can ride for hours without tiring out.

Early Attempts at Electric Bikes

From the beginning, some bicycle inventors toyed with the idea of adding a motor to propel the bicycle without having to pedal. The first attempts used steam power. Gas motors began to be available for bikes in the 1890s and early in the 20th century. Gas-powered bikes originated in Germany and then spread to other countries. In 1894, a German company first introduced the term "motorcycle" and from that point forward gas-powered "bicycles" began their own history, separate and apart from traditional bicycles.

It may surprise you to learn that the first electric bikes appeared in the late 1800s. Multiple patents were filed in both the U.S. and France for electric-powered bikes in the 1890s. In the U.S., Ogden Bolton is often credited as the first to file a patent for an electric-powered bicycle, doing so in 1895.

If the bike boom underway at that time had continued into the early 20th century, it is possible that the development of electric bikes would have happened sooner. Once cars appeared on the scene, however, the enthusiasm for building electric-powered bicycles waned.

Another reason e-bikes didn't become commercially feasible earlier was because the technology wasn't ready yet for what we now think of as electric bikes. A major breakthrough happened in 1989 with the invention of the "pedelec" bike, with a key feature now referred to as "pedal assist."

With a pedelec design, a bike's motor is only triggered when the rider is pedaling, more closely replicating the experience of riding a traditional bicycle. On all previous models, power was controlled only through a throttle and was independent of pedaling. Most e-bikes manufactured today use this pedal-assist design, although in some countries like the U.S. many e-bikes also have a throttle that acts independently of pedaling.

An even larger technology hurdle throughout the 20th Century was the battery for powering an e-bike. Today's modern lithium-ion batteries on e-bikes may seem heavy, but they are much lighter and far more efficient than their predecessors, including lead-acid and NiCad batteries. Earlier e-bikes using those batteries were heavy and provided a relatively short riding range compared with e-bikes using today's lithium batteries. E-bikes with old-technology lead-acid batteries continue to be sold in parts of Asia for very price-conscious consumers.

With the cost of lithium batteries dropping even as their efficiency increases, lithium batteries will likely remain the dominant choice for most e-bikes, at least until an even-better technology emerges.

Despite the technological challenges, several companies attempted to market e-bikes during the second half of the 20th century, but given the factors above and the lack of consumer demand, none of these early models proved successful. While many were designed by private inventors, large corporations including Philips, Panasonic, Sanyo, and Yamaha all marketed e-bikes at some point during the 1970s, 80s, and 90s.

Lee Iacocca's EV Global e-bikes were slow, heavy, and had limited range by modern standards, but for the time they were innovative, stylish, and competitively priced.

One of the more famous names in the commercial development of electric bikes was Lee Iacocca, who is far better known for his contributions to the automotive industry, first as an executive at Ford Motor Company and later as CEO at Chrysler Corporation. In 1997, several years after retiring from his successful automotive career, Iacocca formed EV Global Motors to design and sell electric bicycles and scooters. By today's standards, EV Global's e-bikes were slow, heavy, and had limited range, but for their day they were innovative, stylish, and competitively priced. Even though Iacocca was ahead of his time and the company eventually failed, EV Global Motors left its mark on the development of the modern electric bike.

Boomers Power the Demand for E-Bikes Today

While e-bikes might never have been commercially successful without advancements such as pedal assist and better batteries, demographics has also played a role in e-biking's recent popularity. **The same Baby Boomer generation that created a bike boom in the 1970s is once again fueling demand for bikes of all types, especially electric-powered ones.**

As the Boomer generation moves into retirement, they are redefining what it means to be a senior citizen. As Pedego Electric Bike's Co-Founder and CEO Don DiCostanzo said in this book's introduction, Boomers are the "forever young generation." They are exercising, staying active, enjoying the outdoors, and having the time of their lives. Electric bikes have replaced the rocking chair as the symbol for this active new generation of retirees.

Sales statistics confirm the powerful impact of senior adults on the success of e-bikes. A 2017 survey from the National Institute for Transportation and Communities (NITC) and Portland State University reported that 67.2 percent of electric bike owners in the U.S. were age 45 or older. A UK study found 65 percent of e-bike owners in that country were age 55 or over. Pedego says its typical customer is age 57-58 but many are much older. Another e-bike brand whose customers skew toward the higher age group, Evelo Electric Bicycles, says 81.5 percent of its e-bike customers are over the age of 55.

"There's a younger generation beginning to buy our bikes, but our sweet spot is still the aging Baby Boomer," DiCostanzo said.

The Future of Cycling and E-Bikes

In much of the past century, bicycles were largely regarded, at least in the U.S. and Canada, as either toys for children or exercise machines for athletes and racers. Other adult consumers may have owned a bicycle but rarely rode it. Today, that perception is changing as bikes are being more accepted as a serious transportation choice for adults, especially in larger urban areas where bikes are increasingly being used by commuters and business delivery services.

North America is finally beginning to catch up with Europe, where at least in some countries the bicycle has been a more integral part of the culture. In places like the Netherlands and Denmark, bikes are widely used by people of all ages for daily transportation and as a substitute for cars for short trips. The same can be said for many highly urbanized Asian cultures, where bikes are far more common on city streets than in the U.S. and Canada.

The future of cycling looks promising, both in North America and worldwide. Just look at these statistics:

- **The bicycle industry worldwide is large, generating annual revenues of $45 billion. The U.S. bike market alone is expected to grow to $8 billion annual revenue by 2025.**

- **More than 2.5 times as many bicycles as automobiles are built each year worldwide, and in recent decades that gap has widened.**

- **Copenhagen announced in 2016 that, for the first time in its history, bicycles outnumbered cars on its streets.**

- **In the U.S., the number of bike rides taken annually more than doubled over the past generation to more than four billion.**

- **Recognizing the potential for growth and profits, some well-known automotive and motorcycle companies are getting into e-bike production, including Ducati, Harley-Davidson, Jeep, Mercedes-Benz, Porsche and Yamaha.**

Electric bikes account for a significant amount of the growth in the worldwide bicycle industry. As recently as 2015, in the U.S. and Europe (combined), e-bikes only accounted for 1 of every 18 new bikes manufactured. By 2020, e-bikes accounted for 1 of every 6 new bikes sold in the U.S. and Europe. By 2030, according to the National Bicycle Dealers Association (U.S.), e-bikes will account for nearly 1 of every 3 new bikes built in the U.S. and Europe. If you look only at Europe, projections show that e-bike sales will meet or exceed the sale of traditional bikes by 2030. Already in the Netherlands, e-bike sales to adults now outnumber the annual sale of traditional bikes.

Unlike the short-lived bike boom of the 1890s, this time the popularity of cycling is likely to be more long-lasting. The recent growth in bike sales is built on a more solid foundation. Bicycling has found its place in everyday life. It's not only here to stay, but odds are favorable that bike ownership and usage will continue to grow.

Cycling is also helping make life on this planet better. Here are some of the many benefits of cycling:

- **Reduces traffic congestion in major urban areas.**

- **Provides new economic benefits and jobs.**

- **Reduces air pollution and contributes to the fight against climate change.**

- **Leads to a healthier, happier populace, fighting a myriad of health problems ranging from diabetes to obesity.**

- **Gives older adults and people with certain mobility and health challenges a way to stay more active, fit, and engaged in life.**

- **Creates rewarding new travel and tourism opportunities.**

While e-bikes won't be the full story in the future of cycling on our planet, it's a safe prediction that they will play an increasingly prominent role in bike sales and usage. If you look a decade ahead, it's not hard to imagine a world in which e-bikes may well become the norm for the majority of adult cyclists.

In future chapters, I will explore some of the reasons for the recent worldwide growth in cycling. For senior adults especially, the commercial success of the electric bike has played a significant role in the current bike boom.

Before moving ahead to Chapter 4, be sure to read the fascinating Rider Profile about Ray Marentette starting on the next page. He founded a Facebook group for cycling enthusiasts age 80 and above, with an ever-growing and global membership. Yes, you read that correctly. His unique Facebook group serves as an exclusive club only for cyclists in their 80s and beyond. What more proof do you need that cycling is indeed an activity many seniors can continue to enjoy very late in life! 👓

Ray Marentette

Octogenarian Cyclists Prove You're Never Too Old to Ride

"I believe that staying active keeps you alive,"

- David Hobbs, fellow, Royal Academy of Octogenarian Cyclists

When Ray Marentette, who is in his 80s, got the idea in late 2019 to start a Facebook group for bicyclists age 80 and over, it was in part because he didn't know any other cyclists who were his age.

"...there's a part of the brain that has to be maintained to give you equilibrium and balance. In cycling, you have that."
- Ray Marentette

"I don't know of another 80-year-old who cycles," Ray recalls thinking at the time. "But there's got to be some out there."

So began The Royal Academy of Octogenarian Cyclists, a fun and lofty name for the Facebook group Ray launched. It now numbers more than 500 members from countries spanning the globe, including the United States, Canada, the UK, Scotland, Denmark, the Netherlands, Spain, Greece, and Australia.

Cycling in your 80s and even beyond is not as rare as you might think. The popularity of Ray's group proves it. Many of the group's members are remarkably fit and passionate about cycling.

Take Tom Swanson, of Tucson, Arizona, for example. To celebrate his 83rd birthday, Tom completed an 83-mile bike ride on The Loop, a trail that circles Tucson. Never mind that the temperature was 104 degrees, with hardly any shade. Like many of the more avid octogenarian cyclists, Tom rides his bike nearly every day, year-round. Each year, he gets with some friends and completes a 400-to-500-mile bike tour. He also competes each year in the 50- or 100-mile El Tour DE Tucson. At age 74, Tom rode his bike from coast to coast, solo, across the USA.

Another "fellow" in the Royal Academy, who lives in mountainous Colorado, recently rode a 64-mile trek that included an elevation gain of 3,730 feet. He completed the ride in just 5 1/2 hours. Another fellow rode 32 miles in a day through scenic New England. Yet another fellow, who lives in Central Florida, averaged a fast 19.8 mph on a 22-mile bike ride. That's double the speed of your average neighborhood leisure bike rider, and an impressive performance at any age.

"I believe that staying active keeps you alive," said Royal Academy fellow David Hobbs, who lives in Mission Viejo, California. David rides four days per week, averaging about 30 miles per ride. Since he began tracking his miles on the Strava app in 2013, David said he's ridden more than 45,000 miles.

"My children can't believe how much I ride," David said, describing himself as someone who has always taken fitness seriously.

The group even includes a few nonagenarians – bike riders in their 90s.

A Close-Knit Group

Had it not been for Ray Marentette's dream late last year to start the Royal Academy, most of these age 80-plus cyclists would not know of one another and would have missed a wonderful opportunity to build friendships with their peers. In fact, Ray said the group has evolved into much more than just a Facebook page about bicycling. It's become a community, where birthdays are celebrated, members who lose their spouses are consoled, and where members can talk about their health and other challenges.

"It didn't occur to me that it would become such a close-knit group," Ray said. "There's a great sense of camaraderie, a great sense of 'we've made it this far, guys, so let's celebrate our achievement of living.' I'm really enjoying the communication with these people, because now it's like my world is not this neighborhood any more; it's the whole world."

Ray and his wife Jeanne live in Port Credit, a lakefront community that is part of the City of Mississauga, in Ontario, Canada. Even before starting a Facebook group for bicyclists age 80 and up, Ray already had a reputation as a cyclist and organizer. A few years ago, he began a bike riding group in his town called the Port Credit Slow Roll that rides every two weeks during the warm months, although it unfortunately had to suspend rides during the COVID-19 virus pandemic.

"My bike stayed down in the basement for two years," Ray said, explaining why he started the Port Credit Slow Roll back in 2018. "The tires were flatter than a pancake. I wanted to ride every year, so I said 'this is the year, I'm going to ride my bike.' But my dear wife said 'you're 81 years old and you're too old to ride a bike by yourself.' I didn't want to get hurt on my bike and her say 'I told you so.' Anyway, she said I would really prefer you to not ride by yourself. So, I went to my trusty little computer and printed out a notice: 'Meet me at Saddington Park at 7 o'clock next Thursday. We're going for a bike ride.' We ended up going on our first ride with 13 people. Two weeks later, there were 26. Two weeks after that, it was 48. Then it was 60. It just mushroomed."

Benefits Of Cycling For Senior Adults

Ray believes that cycling is an excellent activity for senior adults.

"As we age, there's a real problem with balance. The greatest number of problems that aging people have is losing their balance and falling, and maybe breaking their hips. It's the start of the end for a lot of people. One of the biggest things about cycling is that there's a part of the brain that has to be maintained to give you equilibrium and balance. In cycling, you have that. You maintain the development of that part of your brain that controls your balance."

When asked how long he plans to keep riding his bike, Ray has a simple answer:

"Forever, for as long as I can get on it and go." ⬌

"You're not exhausted. You're not afraid of the return ride. You know you can get back home. Anytime you see a decline, you don't worry about going back up it."

DR. MIRYAM LIBERMAN (PAGE 62)

CHAPTER 4

Pedaling Your Way to Better Health

"I don't ride a bike to add days to my life. I ride a bike to add life to my days."

– *Unknown*

"You can't be sad while riding a bicycle."

– *Unknown*

"Bicycling unites physical harmony coupled with emotional bliss to create a sense of spiritual perfection that combines one's body, mind and soul into a single moving entity."

– *Frosty Wooldridge, adventurer, author, and cyclist*

After 20 surgeries that left her largely disabled, Dr. Miryam Liberman described herself as being a "physical mess" just a few years ago.

Then she discovered electric-assist bicycles, and her life began to change for the better. Her health improved the more she rode. Today, she's riding 100 to 150 miles per week and has participated in long-distance, multi-day group bike rides.

"If I can do this as a physical mess, starting at age 60 or 62, then I really think nearly anybody can do it."

The rising popularity of cycling and especially electric-assist bicycles during the past decade has been nothing short of revolutionary for the health and welfare of a growing number of middle-age and senior adults like Dr. Miryam. You can read the Rider Profile following this chapter to learn more about Dr. Miryam and her cycling story.

A Cycling Fitness Pioneer: Dr. Paul Dudley White

Today, the health benefits of cycling are well documented, but that was not always the case. One of the earliest proponents of bicycling for fitness was the late renowned cardiologist, Dr. Paul Dudley White (left).

An advocate for both walking and cycling, Dr. White rose to national prominence in the United States after treating President Dwight Eisenhower for a heart attack in 1955. At that time conventional wisdom within cardiology was that patients needed rest and that too much exercise might harm the heart. Dr. White believed otherwise, and assigned the President an exercise routine that included cycling as part of his rehabilitation. President Eisenhower not only recovered but the next year ran for a second term in office.

"If bicycling can be restored to the daily life of all Americans, it can be a vital step toward rebuilding health and vigor in all of us," said Dr. White, who was a co-founder of the American Heart Association. His advocacy for exercise and cycling was a factor in the increased popularity of biking during the 1960s and 1970s.

Thanks in part to his promotion of cycling, annual bike sales in the U.S. hit a peak in 1972 that was not reached again for more than 25 years.

The Amazing Benefits of Cycling

It is hard to name another exercise that the average person can do that has as many benefits to one's health as bicycling. It's no surprise that people who competitively ride bikes on a consistent basis are rarely obese and have more energy than the rest of us. They have to be fit and trim to squeeze into those Spandex biking outfits! Fortunately for the rest of us, we can still enjoy cycling's health benefits even if we're not Lance Armstrong wannabes.

Here are some of the many ways bicycling is good for your health:

Overall health and longevity: An English study found that the average cyclist has the fitness profile of someone 10 years younger, a lower body mass index, and a two-year higher life expectancy compared to non-cyclists. This study defined an average cyclist as someone who rides 45 minutes on a bike at least three times a week, an easily achievable goal even for most senior adults.

Easy on the joints: Aging joints can be painful and prevent many seniors from doing exercises such as walking or jogging. Cycling, on the other hand, is a low-impact sport, easy on the joints. It is said that if you can walk half a mile, then you can ride five miles. Not only does cycling put less stress on joints but it builds up muscles in the legs and glutes that support your joints.

Improves cardiovascular fitness: It is well known that cycling is good for your heart and arteries. Cycling gets your heart pumping faster and the blood circulating better, improving your entire cardiovascular system. Cycling lowers your blood pressure and can reduce your risk of a heart attack or stroke. According to research conducted by the American Heart Association, women who ride at least 20 miles per week have a 50 percent lower risk of developing heart disease. **The AHA also found that bike riding, even as little as 30 minutes per**

week, reduces the risk of developing cardiovascular disease.

This is why Dr. Paul Dudley White, one of the best-known cardiologists in America during the 1950s and 1960s, was such a staunch advocate for cycling. He rode a bike regularly and did so into his 80s. If cardiovascular fitness is one of your goals, be sure to pedal vigorously for at least a portion of each ride to get your heart pumping at an optimal level, just as you would need to walk vigorously to maximize the gains from walking.

Reduces cancer risk: In North America, cancer is the number two killer behind cardiovascular disease. Regular cycling has been shown to reduce the risk of developing certain types of cancer. A University of Glasgow study showed that daily cycling (30 miles or more per week) could reduce cancer risk by 45 percent. Another larger study reported in The Lancet based on 25 years of census data in England and Wales showed a smaller but still significant correlation between regular cycling and cancer risk. This study found that cyclists have an 11 percent lower risk of contracting cancer and a 16 percent lower risk of dying from cancer.

Helps with weight loss: As you read Rider Profiles throughout this book and see quotes from senior riders, a common thread is that they have lost weight thanks to riding their bikes. Cycling burns calories, builds muscle, and shrinks body fat. When done regularly and combined with a sensible diet, cycling can help you lose weight or maintain a proper weight. Want an extra incentive? Dedicated cyclists who ride longer distances say a related benefit is that you can splurge and eat more food on days when you ride without gaining weight, thanks to the hundreds of extra calories you will burn.

Prevents or controls Diabetes: Diabetes is a growing health threat. The International Diabetes Federation says 1 in 10 adults will experience diabetes by 2040. This is in large part due to poor diet and a sedentary lifestyle. In a report on preventing diabetes, technogym. com said the following: "One of the most suitable sports for those suffering from diabetes has proved to be cycling, since it is an aerobic activity, of a repetitive and constant type." A large Danish study found that those who start cycling after age 50 reduce their risk of Type 2 diabetes by 20 percent.

Reduce risk of falls: A major risk as we age is falling, potentially resulting in broken hips or other bones. Cycling can reduce the risk of falling in senior adults. Why? Riding a bike strengthens muscles such as legs and glutes, helping seniors to fight the normal pattern of deteriorating muscle strength that comes with aging. Cycling also improves our balance and coordination.

Cycling is good for your lungs: Many seniors suffer from reduced lung function and breathing issues. Cycling isn't necessarily a cure but regular cycling has been shown to increase lung capacity and overall lung health.

Sleep better: Regular exercise such as cycling helps you sleep better. A Stanford University study of those suffering from insomnia found that a 20-minute daily bike ride reduced by half the time that it took participants to fall asleep at night. Besides the general benefits of exercise, cycling exposes you to daylight and helps restore your circadian rhythm.

Look younger with improved muscles and skin tone: Cycling can help you look (and feel) younger. It is well known for producing tighter glutes and toned leg muscles. Not as well known is that cycling also improves skin health. Cycling increases circulation, bringing more oxygen and nutrients to the skin, which in turn slows the effects of skin aging and wrinkles. Sweating while exercising also flushes harmful toxins from your body.

Numerous other studies have documented the health benefits of cycling. One major, five-year study released in 2017 of 236,450 participants found that cyclists who regularly commute by bike to work had a 52 percent lower risk of succumbing to heart disease than non-cyclists, and a 40 percent lower chance of dying from cancer.

Imagine the positive impact on a nation's public health if even more people chose to ride their bikes regularly, whether commuting to work, running errands, or just cruising on neighborhood streets and nearby trails. Imagine how much money could be saved that is now being spent to fight medical ailments that may be preventable (at least in part) through active exercise such as cycling.

Cycling's Impact on Depression, Mood, Dementia, and More

The benefits of cycling don't stop with the physical ones. Regular cycling improves brain function, outlook, and general mental health. **As we age, cycling can result in improved memory and mental sharpness. It fights depression. It lifts our mood.**

A Duke University study found that pedaling a bicycle creates a spike in serotonin, the "happy hormone." Those who cycle regularly can attest to the natural high they receive when cycling. Some liken it to an almost spiritual feeling of happiness and well-being. Cycling is often suggested as part of a treatment program for stress relief and mild depression.

As we age, our brains normally shrink and we gradually lose some cognitive abilities. Cycling can slow down this process. The exertion of cycling pushes more blood, oxygen and nutrients into the brain, firing up the neurons and resulting in the creation of new brain cells. Cycling has also been found useful for people dealing with disorders such as Parkinson's Disease and ADHD. Not that cycling is a cure, but it can help patients better manage their conditions. Studies have shown that brain activity improves in patients while cycling.

While at this time there is no cure for Alzheimer's Disease and other forms of dementia, cycling can play a role in prevention and treatment. Cycling is believed to improve one's odds of avoiding age-related dementia, or at least of slowing its progression. This is due to cycling's positive impacts on brain function and memory. Active exercise, including cycling, is often encouraged for dementia patients. For more advanced sufferers, specially made tandem bikes can keep patients outdoors and pedaling, with the assistance of a co-rider.

Cycling's Positive Impact on Public Health

The more we as a society can encourage people to walk and ride bicycles, the healthier we will be. This means lower healthcare costs, fewer disabilities, and reduced time lost to rehabilitation and recovery from illnesses and accidents. Imagine the impact on a nation's public health spending if the majority of its adult citizens rode bikes regularly. In the U.S., imagine the favorable impact on the Medicare health insurance program for seniors if most of us Baby Boomers cycled more often.

A recent study conducted by epidemiological researchers at Colorado University gives us a small glimpse into what is possible. It studied the impact of bike-share programs concentrated in a handful of major U.S. cities. While there are only about 100,000 bikes nationwide in these bike-share programs, the study concluded that they are saving the country's healthcare system $36 million annually. By getting people out of their cars and onto bicycles, the study says active bike-share participants in the future are less likely to suffer from serious health conditions including cancer, dementia, and heart disease.

We'd love to see some helmets here, but in every other respect the Netherlands – especially in city centers like Amsterdam – provides an excellent view of how cycling (and developing around a cycling-safe infrastructure) can positively impact overall lifestyle.

This study is a small sample, but just imagine the potential if nations like the U.S. that have not traditionally been bike-friendly would begin to focus more policy, promotion, and infrastructure spending into encouraging widespread, safe cycling by citizens of all ages.

What We Can Learn From the Netherlands

Nowhere are bicycles more a part of the lifestyle than in the Netherlands. With an excellent network of safe bike paths and other infrastructure, the Dutch people ride their bikes everywhere, including to school, work, and on shopping errands. People of all ages ride bikes in the Netherlands, from school children to the elderly. A recent study by Elliot Fishman, Paul Schepers, and Carlijn Kamphuis found that, due to cycling, about 11,000 deaths are prevented each year in the Netherlands and Dutch people have half a year longer life expectancy than the average European. People in the Netherlands live nearly two years longer on average than people in the United States. The nation's sizable investment in building better cycling infrastructure is proving to produce a highly positive cost-benefit ratio in terms of improved public health.

Is it coincidental or not that the Netherlands also ranks highly each year in the United Nations' World Happiness Index? Does cycling play a role in this high ranking? In the 2021 report, the Netherlands ranked No. 5 among all nations. Canada was No. 14, the UK ranked No. 17, and the United States followed at No. 18.

Would we be a happier nation if we rode our bikes more?

Rider Profiles Attest to Health Benefits

As you continue to read the Rider Profiles throughout this book, you will see that many senior cyclists comment on how cycling has helped them lose weight or otherwise improve their health. Following this chapter, I think you will be especially inspired by the story of Dr. Miryam Liberman. Her e-bike has played a major role in her health recovery.

Then, in Chapter 5, I will look at the exercise benefits of e-bikes, a controversial topic among cyclists these days. As an e-bike cyclist, you will really want to read Chapter 5. It will equip you with the facts you need to know about how e-bikes can generate an impressive amount of exercise benefit. It will also help you respond to misinformed critics who, for some odd reason, seem compelled to tell you that your e-bike is of no value to your health. They are wrong, as you will see.

Dr. Miryam Liberman

How Her E-Bike Helped Her Overcome Major Health Challenges

"(My e-bike) changed my whole life. I just can't say enough about it. My bike is like the love of my life. It allows you such freedom."

- Dr. Miryam Liberman

Retired physician **Dr. Miryam Liberman, 67,** has had more than her share of health problems. It would have been easy for her to have concluded that cycling, or really any form of active exercise, was just too hard for her. "I have had over 20 surgeries including my knee and back. I became pretty disabled," Dr. Miryam said.

Her parents were Holocaust survivors in Poland, and from them Dr. Miryam learned that when life hands you a challenge, you don't give up. You find a way to keep moving forward. So rather than surrender to her health problems, at age 62 she turned to e-bikes.

"When I started riding, I was absolutely terrified. I was so disabled when I started riding. I had very poor balance. It took me six to eight months to get my confidence up, but since then I have ridden over 14,000 miles."

Like so many senior adults who have rediscovered cycling, and especially electric-powered bikes, the experience has been life-changing for Dr. Miryam. In her final three years of employment, she used her e-bike to commute to work in Westlake Village, California, where she practiced internal medicine. The round-trip commute was about 25 miles.

She described her commute as "moving meditation," taking her through a mix of Southern California urban and wildlife landscapes and through Hidden Valley.

From that point forward, riding her e-bike has become an integral part of Dr. Miryam's lifestyle.

"It changed my whole life," Dr. Miryam said of her Pedego Interceptor e-bike, made by Pedego Electric Bikes. "I just can't say enough about it. My bike is like the love of my life. It allows you such freedom."

Now retired, Dr. Miryam still rides an average of 100 to 150 miles per week, using her e-bike to run errands as well as doing longer rides, her favorite being about 50 miles.

"By incorporating the bike into your commuting, shopping, meeting up with friends, it's so fun to ride that you will keep conniving with what more you can do on the bike because it's so much fun."

She credits her e-bike with significantly improving her health and adding to her enjoyment of life.

"Having the e-bike suddenly seemed to solve all my problems. You have technology to give you wings. It gives you mobility. I can't run, I can't walk on a hard surface ... but you don't stop dreaming of being alive. If you're not moving, you're not active, you're not going to feel as good, you're not going to sleep as well, you're not going to be as happy and healthy. The human body was meant to move and love and be with people and innovate and take care of each other. I never stopped dreaming."

Not only does Dr. Miryam ride her e-bike around her Southern California community, she and her husband, Avi Benami, take their bikes with them when they travel. They carried their bikes on a 5,500-mile road trip and were able to ride in the Tetons, the north rim of the Grand Canyon, Aspen (Colorado), and national parks such as Utah's Bryce National Park.

Dr. Miryam has also pushed herself by participating in physically challenging, long-distance charity bike rides that required months of training. She rode in The Climate Ride through Glacier National Park in Montana and Waterton National Park in Canada. It was a grueling 250-mile ride over four days through rugged terrain, traveling as much as 100 miles in a single day. At 65, she was the oldest rider there. She remembers one particular day where they rode through nearly 50 miles of solid hail and rain, with chilly 44-degree temperatures and 45-mph gusts, making it feel much colder. Her training and research paid off, allowing her to successfully complete the run.

As a physician, Dr. Miryam has studied the health benefits of cycling and particularly e-bikes. She's convinced that e-bikes can greatly improve a senior adult's health and overall well being.

"There are many medical articles that say electric bikes give you the same workout (as conventional bikes). They've hooked people up to monitors. They find the average is about 85 to 95 percent of the workout on an e-bike versus a conventional bike. However, they do it twice as much because they love it. It (e-bike) gives you nearly the same medical workout for your heart, your brain, and your immune system, but ironically you kinda get hooked and you do it more, so it winds up being a greater benefit."

One reason e-bikes are such good exercise is because people *want* to ride them, Dr. Miryam said. They are fun. E-bike owners tend to ride more often and ride farther per ride. "Your e-bike is not going to sit in your garage. You're going to be riding it."

Because people enjoy their e-bike experience so much, they sometimes don't even think about the fitness aspects of it.

"The e-bike is stealth exercise," Dr. Miryam said. "You get 85 to 95 percent of the cardiovascular benefits, but you don't feel like you're doing it."

For seniors especially, Dr. Miryam said e-bikes remove some of the fear and apprehension older riders have had in the past with conventional bicycles.

"You're not exhausted. You're not afraid of the return ride. You know you can get back home. Anytime you see a decline, you don't worry about going back up it."

Not only is riding an e-bike good for your physical health, Dr. Miryam said it's good for your social and mental health too.

"You wind up living more, seeing more, being more fit, being more socially engaged. I saw things (riding her e-bike) I never saw before. Exhibits and gardens. And you can smell it. You can't

smell it in a car. You see things in your neighborhood you've never seen before."

Dr. Miryam hopes her example of riding actively now after years of disability and multiple surgeries will encourage others to try e-bikes.

"If I can do it as a physical mess, starting at age 60 or 62, then I really think nearly anybody can do it." 👓

The Surprising Exercise Benefits of Electric Bikes; Why Riding an E-bike Isn't 'Cheating'

"I hate to exercise, but I love to ride my e-bike!"
– 64-year-old cancer survivor, quoted from Facebook

"After not cycling for decades I bought an e-trike a year and a half ago. I put over 2,500 km (1,553 miles) on it. I'm 79."
– Facebook senior cyclist

Like many of us Baby Boomers, Jon Treffert said he fondly recalls riding his bicycle as a child and commuting to classes on a bicycle while attending graduate school in Madison, Wisconsin. But then adult life and the demands of his career pushed his bike days aside. He didn't ride a bike again for 30 years. Over those decades he gained too much weight. He was diagnosed with Type 2 diabetes. He was taking more prescription drugs.

One day, when Jon stepped on the scales and realized he had hit a new high of 270 pounds, he knew he had to take action. Remembering what good shape he used to be in while riding his bike, Jon began to explore the best bikes for overweight men and for his hilly city of Knoxville, Tennessee. He purchased a Patriot Day6 e-bike and began riding. Three years and more than 11,000 miles of riding later, Jon credits his e-bike and his low-carb, high-fat diet for helping him feel much better and getting back to what he weighed in high school.

"It is not an overstatement to say that this bike changed my life," Jon (left) said. "Beginning on November 4, 2017, at age 60.8 years old, I began a 14-month health journey losing 100 pounds and reversing Type 2 diabetes."

Testimonials like the one above from Jon confirm that you can indeed get excellent exercise results and improve your health riding an e-bike, but as you will find when you talk with other seniors who cycle, this is a controversial topic these days. Hopefully this chapter will help convince you that you don't have to choose between buying a bike for exercise and buying an e-bike.

Is an E-Bike 'Cheating'?

As e-bikes continue to grow in popularity, an increasingly common (and unpleasant) occurrence on social media, or even while riding along bike trails, is for traditional (non-electric) bike owners to criticize e-bike riders as "cheaters." They argue that e-bikes are more akin to motor scooters, not bicycles, and have little exercise value and no place on bike trails. It's an ongoing discussion that can get rather testy at times.

Why one bicyclist would dare to say something so mean-spirited and insensitive to a fellow cyclist they don't even know is beyond my comprehension, but sadly it happens. One senior female cyclist says a person pulled up to her and asked if she was riding an e-bike. When she said yes, the person went into a rant, calling her a "phony" and saying her bike was "fake." What this rude person did not know is that the e-bike cyclist he was shouting at was a two-time cancer survivor without the strength to ride a traditional bike. Her e-bike was greatly improving her quality of life, adding exercise, fresh air, and pleasure.

By the way, the next time someone on a non-electric bike raises the "cheater" allegation, ask him or her if their bike has gears. If so, isn't that cheating too? Wouldn't a one-speed bike provide a better workout? Why are they riding a bike at all? Why not walk? Better yet, ask them if they've read the book, *E-bikes - Putting the fun Back Into Cycling (and Life) at any age.*

Those "cheater" comments may be fueled by ignorance, hostility, or maybe by a twinge of jealousy, but a growing body of scientific research is confirming that e-bikes do indeed offer significant exercise benefits. In fact, as you will see in this chapter, e-bikes provide nearly the same exercise value as traditional bikes. Plus, e-bikes offer the added bonus of being easier to ride for senior adults — and a lot more fun.

These findings are good news for all of us Baby Boomers who are riding e-bikes or considering buying one. We are definitely not "cheaters."

Several large-scale scientific studies have been conducted to assess the exercise value of e-bikes. These include academic studies from the Netherlands, Norway, the European Union, and the United States. Their conclusions are remarkably similar and can be summarized as follows:

E-bike cyclists are not necessarily replacing traditional cyclists but more often are new cyclists. This is certainly true among seniors, who as Jon Treffert mentioned earlier in this chapter, had not ridden a bicycle in 30 years. Many of us who are taking up e-bikes were not cycling previously and would not otherwise be cycling at all.

Thus, the argument over whether a person is getting more exercise on one type of bicycle versus another type misses the point. **The typical e-bike cyclist, especially when it comes to senior adults, is getting new and valuable exercise he or she would not be receiving without an electric bike.** In the majority of instances, new e-bike riders are not swapping a traditional bike for an e-bike, but are new to cycling (or haven't cycled in many years). As a result, e-bikes expand the number of total cyclists and mean more people than before are exercising, which is a good thing.

E-bike cyclists ride more per trip and more often than traditional cyclists, gaining as much or even more exercise. Perhaps the most important finding of these studies is that e-bike cyclists tend to ride more miles per trip and ride their bikes more often than do traditional (non-electric) cyclists. While it's true that e-bike cyclists expend less energy per pedal stroke, they make up for it by riding farther, much farther, than the average traditional bicyclist, especially comparing within the same age group. As a result, they receive as much overall exercise as a traditional cyclist, and in many cases actually exercise more.

Think of your typical Baby Boomer, maybe yourself. Somewhere in your garage, covered with cobwebs, is a lonely old bicycle. Rarely, if ever, does it get dusted off and used. When you do ride it, you tire out quickly, especially if your locale has hills, and you quickly return home, tired, exhausted, and not looking forward to your next ride.

Now contrast this with your typical senior adult who owns an e-bike. These Boomers can't wait for their next ride because it's so much fun. They will ride farther and farther, not eager to stop, because the pedal assist allows them to ride longer and conquer hills without tiring out.

So who is getting the superior exercise experience in this example? Obviously, it's the e-bike rider. Not only that, but the e-bike rider is happier and enjoying the mental health benefits described in Chapter 4.

As one senior e-bike cyclist summed up in a comment on a Facebook post recently, "It's half as much work but I ride 10 times as long as I did on my regular bike, and I'm smiling at the end. Win-Win."

E-bikes make cycling possible for groups who could not otherwise cycle. E-bikes make it possible for many older adults to ride despite their decreased stamina, joint problems, and the general effects of aging. They are enjoying exercise and the outdoors to a degree that would not otherwise be possible. **Beyond seniors, e-bikes open up the potential for cycling for a broad range of people of all ages who suffer from a variety of health challenges.** According to data reported by Juiced Bikes, one in four e-bike riders reports having physical impairments that keep them from riding a standard bicycle. Without a doubt, e-bikes have significantly improved the quality of life for these people.

One U.S. company, Electric Bike Technologies, has given away several of its popular Liberty Trikes to children suffering from spinal muscular atrophy (SMA), a genetic disorder that causes muscle weakness and atrophy. While some of these children cannot walk a block without tiring out, they can ride for miles on an electric-powered Liberty Trike. Jason Kraft, CEO of Electric Bike Technologies, decided to make it a point to identify the children most in need and gift them a trike. You can read more about the Liberty Trike and other electric trikes in Chapter 8.

E-bikes get adults out of their cars for short errands, resulting in more exercise. Studies show that some e-bike owners are using their bikes as a car substitute, especially for running short errands. I myself have made numerous trips by e-bike to a local grocery store, about two miles from my home, or to other nearby businesses to enjoy a smoothie or fast-food meal.

I know of another senior adult who, before retiring, cycled seven miles each way to work and back on his e-bike. Especially as cities work to improve and expand bike infrastructure, including bike trails and lanes, more people are finding that an e-bike makes a good substitute for a car for short errands. In heavily congested urban areas, riding a bike may actually be faster than traveling by car, bus, or taxi. The end result is that more adults are getting more exercise, thanks to their e-bikes.

A Closer Look at the Research Data

Several large-scale, academic studies have looked at the question of whether e-bikes provide sufficient exercise. Let's take a look at the research findings.

One study conducted by researchers at the University of Zurich in Switzerland surveyed 8,600 cyclists, including e-bike cyclists, across Europe. Among other things, the study examined the energy used by traditional cyclists versus e-bike cyclists and the typical length of their cycling trips. It used the Metabolic Equivalents of Task (MET) measurement, which is a standard value of physical activity intensity. Walking, for instance, requires 4 METs. The study found riding an e-bike uses 5 METs and cycling 6.8 METs.

That would seem to give the advantage to regular (non-electric) cycling – but wait, there's more. The study further found that the average trip per rider on an e-bike was considerably longer than the average trip on a traditional bike. It concluded that both regular and e-bikes offer a similar exercise benefit.

A study in Norway also confirmed that e-bike riders go farther per ride and ride more frequently. It found that e-bike users increased their distance traveled by bike from 2.1 kilometers (1.3 miles) to 9.2 kilometers (5.7 miles) per day, a significant increase. Further, it found that e-bike owners increased their use of their bike for meeting daily transportation needs (commuting and running errands) from 17 percent to 49 percent. This means e-bike riders more often chose their e-bike over driving or using public transportation.

Research led by the University of Bristol in the UK and published in the International Journal of Behavioral Nutrition and Physical Activity (IJBNPA) compared walking, traditional biking, and riding an e-bike, measuring exercise results over the same distance. Not surprisingly, it found that e-bike riding is better cardiovascular exercise than walking but not as good as riding a conventional bike. No adjustment was made for the fact that in real-life situations those with e-bikes are likely to ride farther and more often. The study's authors made the point that any form of exercise is preferable to being sedentary. In the case of senior adult e-bike riders that is often the alternative — either not exercising at all or walking. Clearly, riding an e-bike is an improvement over either of those alternatives.

Similar results were found in another Norwegian study also published in the International Journal of Behavioral Nutrition and Physical Activity. It found that e-bike riders were 8.5 times more active than someone at rest, whereas traditional bike riders were 10.9 times more active, not a large gap. E-bike riders used 51 percent of lung capacity while cycling compared with 58 percent for traditional cyclists, only a 13 percent difference.

Another study by Ron Wensel, an engineer and cyclist, compared heart rates and calories burned by traditional and e-bike cyclists during a one-hour ride over relatively hilly terrain, with the e-bike cyclist using the throttle for assist on the more hilly portions of the route. An e-biker burned 444 calories per hour, compared with the regular bike where the rider burned 552 calories. That's only a 20 percent difference between the two types of cyclists, and regardless, even burning 444 calories per hour is significant exercise.

While not mentioned in Ron's study, another important fact to consider is how many of us senior adults are going to ride for one hour on that hilly terrain using a regular bike? Not many. And if we ride it once on a regular bike, with considerable sweat and effort, how eager are we going to be to make a habit of it? By contrast, we're much more likely to keep riding the e-bike on this route, even with the hills, and enjoy the experience.

It's obvious from studies like these that e-bike riders are receiving real exercise value, not "cheating". The critics are wrong.

The Story of an 80-Year-Old Newspaper Deliverer

Sometimes a real-life story can make the point better than scientific studies and statistics. The British news media reported recently about an 80-year-old man who had reluctantly decided the time had come for him to retire from his newspaper delivery route in the village of Headcorn in Kent. When Evans Cycles and the Raleigh Bicycle Co. learned of his story, they gave George Bailey an e-bike so he could continue his paper route.

The news brought a smile to his face – and a new purpose to keep living. There's no question that his physical and mental health will get a boost with his new electric bike versus retiring from a job he loves and sitting at home. In one media interview, George said that thanks to the e-bike, he might still be delivering the paper when he turns 90.

George is more proof that e-bikes are life-changing for seniors, enhancing both our physical and mental health.

How to Maximize Your Exercise Benefits Using an E-bike

The evidence is clear and convincing that riding an e-bike is a very good form of exercise. You don't need to feel inferior to anyone when riding your e-bike or e-trike. Besides, most senior e-bike riders will tell you they are having a lot more fun than they would be walking, working out in a gym, or riding a regular bike. Even lap swimming, as great as it is, can be pretty boring. Not so with riding an e-bike. You're outdoors, enjoying the scenery, and seeing other people.

Here are some tips to help you maximize the amount of exercise you receive from your e-bike:

- *Find ways to incorporate your e-bike riding into your daily life, such as using it to run errands, visit friends, or commute to a job.* This will give you more opportunities for exercising.

- *Set a fixed time each day for riding your e-bike.* Find a time of day that works best for you, put on your helmet, and go. Like any form of exercise, keeping to a regular schedule is a good way to be more successful.

- *Keep a log of your riding mileage to motivate you and track your progress.* The easiest way to do this is with a cellphone bike app such as Map My Ride, Strava, Ride With GPS, or Ride Spot. You will be amazed at how your ability to ride longer distances per trip will quickly increase.

- *Find a cycling buddy.* While many of us enjoy the serenity and peace of solo cycling, riding in a group helps us stay motivated, and we may ride more often or longer. If you live in a larger 55+ community, odds are good there's a biking group you can join. If not, ask your local bike shop about local riding clubs or groups.

- ⚙ ***Pedal as much as possible in order to get exercise benefits. E-bikes are meant to be ridden as bicycles, not as scooters.*** Even if your e-bike has a throttle, use it as little as possible. If you are physically able to pedal, do so. Push yourself over time to pedal more and throttle less. At the same time, don't stand in judgment of others who use their throttles more than we may think is appropriate. We don't know their health challenges, which are not always obvious from outward appearances. Perhaps riding a bike or trike using a throttle is the best they can do, and it sure beats sitting home alone watching TV.

- ⚙ ***Wean yourself off of using pedal assist all of the time, or use a lower level of PAS.*** As you ride more and build up leg strength and stamina, you will find you don't need to use pedal assist all of the time. When I ride on flat surfaces, I often turn off my pedal assist (or put it in the "0" setting) and just use my leg power. I don't do this all of the time, but do so when it feels comfortable. This not only increases your exercise exertion but saves your battery, so you can ride longer per charge.

- ⚙ ***Make your e-bike part of your travel and vacation plans.*** I take my e-bike with me almost everywhere I go on car trips. Using apps like Traillink and AllTrails, you can find bike trails near your destination or along your path. There are also organized bike tours available around the country and throughout the world, some of which focus on senior cyclists and are e-bike friendly. Such tours can make for memorable adventures. See the "Resources" section in the back of this book for more information about how to find bike trails near you.

In the Rider Profile following this chapter, you will read about a senior cyclist whose e-bike helped her regain her health and lose weight. Thousands of senior adults who have bought e-bikes have similar stories to share. My hope is that these stories, and this book as a whole, will motivate you to join the e-bike revolution, or get more from it if you already own an e-bike. It will be one of the best things you can do for both your physical and mental health.

Beginning with the next chapter, I will provide you with information to choose the perfect e-bike for your needs and budget. I will share the facts you need to know to be a smarter e-bike consumer, whether you are buying from a local bike shop or online. Even if you already own an e-bike, the next few chapters will give you a better understanding of your bike and how it works. 🕶

Kathy Galloway

Regaining Balance and Losing Weight With an E-bike

"I have lost 55 pounds since the surgery, and I attribute that to a KETO diet and daily e-bike exercise."

– *Kathy Galloway*

Major back surgery affected Kathy Galloway's balance and overall strength, but then she bought her first e-bike, a small, folding style bike. Kathy credits her e-bike, along with a healthy diet, with helping her recover and lose a significant amount of weight.

"I have lost 55 pounds since the surgery, and I attribute that to a KETO diet and daily e-bike exercise," Kathy said.

She and her husband Rick, who rides a regular (not electric) bike, started off slowly, riding 5 to 10 miles per day after Kathy bought the e-bike. They rode on neighborhood streets and a golf cart path near their home in Gilbert, Arizona, a suburb of Phoenix. Gradually, she extended her range to 15 to 20 miles per trip, and the results showed.

"I really regained my balance. That was one of my biggest challenges," Kathy said of her first-year's experience with her e-bike. "Also, since I was pedaling all the time, with pedal assist, I started to regain a lot of the strength in my legs too. I almost always pedal. I try to get as much exercise as possible."

At age 66, Kathy is still working full time, which puts a limit on how often she can fit rides into her schedule, especially during shorter winter days. Nevertheless, she and Rick have already taken a few bike trips and hope to take more. She said they've taken their bikes to national parks like Yellowstone and the Grand Canyon.

Kathy says she's grateful for her Lectric XP e-bike and looks forward to many years of riding ahead. 👓

"It is not an overstatement to say that this bike changed my life."

JON TREFFERT (PAGE 68)

CHAPTER 6
Choosing a Senior-Friendly E-Bike, Part 1

"The bicycle is the noblest invention of mankind."

– William Saroyan, playwright

"Bicycling means simplicity and simplicity means happiness."

– Mehmet Murat Ilkan

The joy of bike riding that we Baby Boomers experience today may be similar to what we felt as children or young adults, but as we are all well aware, our bodies have changed. The bike you rode as a child is obviously not the right style of bicycle for you today, as a senior adult. Even if you rode a bike during your young adult and mid-life years, it too is likely not the right style of bike for you when you're age 60 and over.

Fortunately for us seniors, bike manufacturers have responded with new bikes (and trikes) that have designs and features better suited to more mature adults. This is especially true when it comes to electric-powered bikes and trikes, since one of the larger target markets for these vehicles is the senior-adult market. There's an e-bike (or e-trike) out there that's perfect for you.

In this chapter and the one that follows, I'm going to help you understand the choices available when selecting the right style of bike for you. I won't recommend one brand over another, since there are many fine bikes on the market (and sites such as ElectricBikeReview.com have done so in detail). There is no one bike or brand that is "best" for everyone – it depends entirely on your personal circumstances and preferences.

Choosing a Regular Bike vs. an E-Bike

One of the first decisions you will need to make when shopping for a bike is whether you are OK with a traditional (human-powered only) bicycle or whether you want to buy an electric-powered bike. There's no "right" answer for everyone. The majority of adult bike sales are still traditional (not electric) bikes. There's a dedicated group of very fit senior adults who still ride road bikes. There are many more seniors who ride a variety of styles of regular bikes for everything from neighborhood rides with friends to cross-country touring.

Even so, the percentage of senior adults who are choosing to buy e-bikes instead of a traditional bike is growing rapidly every year. For your average Baby Boomer, an electric bike (or trike) is usually going to be the better choice.

"I think it (an electric bike) is fun," said Court Rye, shown at left, founder and president of ElectricBikeReview.com, which has reviewed more than 1,000 e-bikes since starting in 2012. "It's something to get interested in. It lets you feel kind of young again or keep up with a friend or go out on a longer ride and not worry so much about getting tired or winded or getting a muscle cramp because you know you can get home."

Electric-assist bicycles (e-bikes) are a real game-changer. They make biking fun again. Regardless of age or physical condition, you can ride farther without tiring out. You can conquer hills. You will look forward to your next ride.

What's Different About an E-Bike?

The Pedego Comfort Cruiser. Photo Used With Permission, ©2021, Pedego Electric Bikes

An e-bike looks much like any other bicycle. Unlike a motor scooter, you still pedal an electric bicycle and still get good exercise (see Chapter 4). **What distinguishes an e-bike from a regular bike is that it includes an electric motor, battery, and a controller, or display screen.** The electric motor is usually mounted on the rear wheel, although a growing number of e-bikes, especially at the higher end of the price spectrum, now come with motors mounted in the pedal assembly. These are called mid-drive motors. The large, heavy lithium batteries are usually mounted on either the frame support bar (called the downtube) or behind the seat. Some are located on the rear luggage rack, above the rear wheel. The battery is the most expensive part of an e-bike and definitely deserves your pampering. I will talk about how to care for an e-bike battery in a later chapter.

The motor and battery provide an additional boost to your pedaling. It's like having a special force available on request to assist you. This extra boost is especially helpful when going up hills. This boost is called "pedal assist," often referred to by the acronym PAS. Most e-bikes have multiple levels of pedal assist, anywhere from three to nine. PAS 1 provides only a modest boost and you are still providing most of the forward thrust through pedaling. As you go progressively up the PAS numbers, the assistance you receive from the electric motor gets greater and the bike moves at a faster speed.

Do You Need A Throttle?

Some e-bikes also include a throttle, which makes it possible to ride without pedaling. Throttles are controversial in cycling circles. Some nations, including those in the European Union, either ban throttles altogether or allow only a modest "starter throttle" with a very low top speed. In the U.S. and Canada, most e-bikes have a throttle capable of propelling the bike forward at speeds up to 20 mph (or 28 mph on a Class 3 e-bike) without pedaling. Throttle critics argue that this blurs the line between what is truly a bike versus scooters and mopeds. Some U.S. trails ban Class 2 and Class 3 bikes because they have throttles. (See Chapter 2 for a fuller discussion of the three class designations for e-bikes in the U.S.)

Used properly, a throttle can be of great value to the senior cyclist. A throttle can help you take off from a dead stop more easily, which is even more useful on e-bikes due to their greater weight. It can help you scoot across a busy intersection more quickly. A throttle can help you take a break when you are on a long ride and just need a minute to cruise, throttle only, with no pedaling.

If your health will allow, your goal with an e-bike should be to pedal most of the time. Don't rely on the throttle as your primary means of power. A bicycle is not a motorcycle. On the other hand, the throttle is a handy feature for those seniors who have disabilities that limit their pedaling ability or stamina. If you must use your throttle when riding on busy trails, please be mindful of your speed around pedestrians and other bikes. Not only is too much speed a safety hazard but it can add to the friction between regular cyclists (and pedestrians) and e-bike riders. For the rest of us, let's not be too quick to pass judgment on a fellow e-bike rider who we think uses the throttle too much. We may not know their health limitations. It's at least admirable that they can be outdoors and enjoying riding, even if that means relying on a throttle.

E-Bike Drawbacks

As great as they are for most senior cyclists, e-bikes do have their drawbacks:

- **E-bikes cost considerably more,** typically in the $1,500 to $5,000 range.

- **They are much heavier than traditional bikes,** usually weighing between 50 and 70 pounds. This can make e-bikes more difficult to handle and transport for some seniors.

- **E-bikes will require more maintenance than regular bikes** since they are more complex.

- **Batteries have a limited range per charge, typically anywhere from 20 to 60 miles.** That's more than enough distance for most senior cyclists, but running out of power while still out on a trail can make for a challenging ride back to your home or vehicle.

Whether to purchase a traditional bike or an e-bike is a personal choice. Talk with friends who bike. Consider your health and fitness status. Think about how you will use your bike. Unless you are still a road-warrior athlete who rides one of those sleek road bikes with low handlebars, skinny seat, and thin tires, odds are good that if you are a senior adult you will be happier owning an e-bike. They are ideally suited to the needs of active seniors. You should at least try riding one before making your decision on which type of bike to purchase. Most bike shops will let you test ride bikes, and many stores rent e-bikes.

Buying From a Bike Shop or Online

One of the first decisions you must make is whether to purchase your e-bike from a local bike shop or buy it online. A few years ago, it was hard to find many electric bikes at local bike shops, so consumers had little choice but to shop online. Fortunately, that has changed. On the other hand, the choice of e-bike brands, styles and features is still far greater online, since most local shops only carry a limited number of e-bike brands and models.

So where should you shop for a senior-friendly e-bike? For the average senior adult, I believe you are better off buying from a local bike shop, especially for your first e-bike. Look for a bike shop with a good choice of e-bikes or that sells only e-bikes. Preferably, buy from a shop that understands the needs of senior cyclists, not a shop that caters primarily to the younger road bike crowd or mountain bikers.

When I first got back into biking as a senior, I drove an hour from my home, passing by at least two other local bike shops, to buy from a bike shop located inside a large 55+ community. I knew they would understand my needs and have appropriate "senior-friendly" bikes in stock.

There are many fine independently owned local bike shops that cater to the e-bike market, but **on a national level in the U.S., the** Pedego Electric Bikes **brand is the largest e-bike-only retailer.** Pedego has about 200 local stores, many of them operated by franchise owners who are age 50 plus. Pedego targets the senior-adult market. They have an enthusiastic and loyal owner base. There are many fine e-bike brands out there, but if you are looking for your first e-bike and have a Pedego store nearby, it is worth checking out. (See the Rider Profile on Don DiCostanzo, CEO of Pedego, at the end of this chapter.)

For the average senior adult, bike shops have several advantages:

⚙ **A bike shop can advise you on the right type of bicycle based on your needs, experience, size, and health.**

⚙ **Bike shops will let you test ride various bikes to see what you most like.**

⚙ **Bikes sold at bike shops aren't necessarily of better quality than what you can buy online, but you are far less likely to wind up with a poorly made, unreliable bike at a shop.** They carefully choose the bikes they sell. It's not in their best interest to sell bikes that customers won't like and that won't be reliable.

⚙ **A bike shop will make sure the bike is assembled correctly and properly fitted to you.** Proper fit is extremely important.

⚙ **Finally, bike shops offer after-the-sale service, parts, and warranty work.** This factor alone makes buying locally better for most senior-adult consumers.

On the downside, you will likely pay more for a bike at a local shop versus online, perhaps much more, but the benefits may be worth it for the typical e-bike buyer.

When to Buy Online

While buying through a local bike shop has many advantages, so does buying an e-bike online, sometimes referred to as the direct-to-consumer channel. If you know enough about e-bikes to feel confident about making your own choice, you can find many good-quality e-bikes (and e-trikes) online, often at very competitive prices.

The challenge of selecting an e-bike online is the dizzying number of choices, with literally hundreds of brands and thousands of models. It is hard for the average consumer to know which e-bikes are better quality and which ones will offer after-the-sale service and parts. The onus is on you to do your homework. You can learn a lot by joining one of the many Facebook groups dedicated to cycling, such as "Ebike Cyclists Over 60." Online review services such as Court Rye's ElectricBikeReview.com (EBR) are another good source.

Court says the overall quality of online e-bikes has improved significantly since he first started doing his reviews a decade ago. "I'm less hesitant to recommend buying a bike online now," Court said. "I feel like it can be a great option, understanding that people are price-sensitive, especially if they are getting his and her bikes or something like that."

If you are going to shop online, do *not* shop solely based on price. That's a formula for trouble and disappointment. Trust me, any e-bike selling for just a few hundred dollars on online sites like Amazon is not a decent quality bike that will provide you with good service over a longer period of time. Don't waste your money.

Just like Pedego has emerged as the leading retail force in selling e-bikes in the U.S., Rad Power Bikes is the largest online seller of e-bikes in the U.S. If you are wanting to educate yourself on the various styles of e-bikes, common features, and pricing, Rad's consumer-friendly website is a good place to start. It is one of many direct-to-consumer companies with a wide choice of good-quality e-bikes to choose from.

Avoid Big-Box Retailers

The worst place to buy an e-bike is from a big-box retail company. As a sign of the growing popularity of e-bikes, many large retailers such as Costco, Walmart, and Best Buy have started selling e-bikes. There are at least three reasons why this isn't your best place to shop for an e-bike:

- The brands of e-bikes they carry tend to be lesser-known Asian brands on the lower end of the price and quality scale.

- Store personnel at these retailers aren't trained to help you make a wise choice or to properly assemble and fit the bike for you.

- When you need warranty work or parts, you will be forced to deal directly with the bike company, which is likely based in Asia – and local bike shops may not be willing to repair your bike, in part because of how hard it is to get parts.

E-Trike Conversion Kit. Photo Used With Permission of ElectricTrike.com

What About E-Bike Kits?

A third alternative is to buy an e-bike kit for your existing traditional bicycle, converting it to an e-bike. If you love your current bicycle and it's in good shape, you can save money by adding an e-bike conversion kit to it instead of buying a new e-bike. While this may appeal to do-it-yourself, mechanically-oriented consumers, it's not the best choice for most cyclists.

E-bikes are built differently from regular bikes from the ground up. They have heavier frames, better brakes, and suitable tires. You can convert your old bike into an e-bike, but often it may not perform as well or be as safe to ride.

E-bike conversion kits are more commonly used with trikes (three-wheel bikes). An electric motor with pedal assist makes a trike much easier to pedal. Many bike shops install e-bike conversion kits on new adult and recumbent trikes. Professionally installed e-kits on trikes seem to work well. Electric trikes will be discussed in more detail later in this book.

How Do You Plan To Use The Bike?

I will talk in more detail in the next chapter about types of e-bikes, but when selecting an e-bike it is important to think ahead about how you will use it. Don't buy a fat-tire e-bike just because that's what your best friend has. Maybe she rides her e-bike off-road through sand and dirt, while your riding preference is for neighborhood streets and paved trails. **You need a bike that suits your needs.** "Which bike to buy really comes down to how the bike is going to be used," said EBR's Court Rye.

Know Your Budget, But Be Realistic

One of the worst mistakes a new bike buyer can make is to shop primarily by price, looking for the cheapest bicycle. An e-bike isn't the type of product you want to buy cheaply from Amazon — or from big-box retailers as discussed above. Your safety while riding is at stake, as well as how well the bike will perform and how long it will last. If there was ever a time in life to put quality ahead of price when it comes to buying a bicycle, the senior years is the time. You don't want to get stuck with an e-bike that doesn't perform well, requires frequent repairs, or leaves you stranded out on a lonely trail.

So how much should you expect to pay for an e-bike? **In the U.S. (at the time this book was published) you could find a good selection of electric assist (e-bike) models costing between $1,500 and $6,000.** That's not to say there may not be a few acceptable-quality, lower-end e-bikes for sale for less than $1,500, but if you approach your purchase assuming you will need to pay at least $1,500 (and probably much more), plus tax and accessories, to get the right bike for your needs, you will likely be happier with your purchase.

When shopping for e-bikes, it helps to know that some e-bikes are priced higher because you are buying a more established brand that provides a better warranty and will likely be around later when you need parts and service. You are also buying the expertise and service of a local bike shop and its staff when you choose to buy through a local store instead of online. It may be well worth it for peace of mind to pay extra for these benefits, if your budget allows.

On the high end of the price spectrum, you can pay in the $5,000 to $10,000 range for top-end, premium-quality e-bikes. These are name-brand, full-featured, smooth-riding, well-engineered bikes – and they are mostly sold through bike shops, not online. They will give you a sweet ride, no doubt, and may be the best choice for discriminating buyers who can afford to buy the most state-of-the-art products. (Keep in mind that these were the prices in the U.S. market at the time this book was published in 2021 and may change over time.)

E-Bikes Spur Business Growth

The exploding popularity of e-bikes is creating new business opportunities worldwide. Here in the U.S., numerous new companies have formed to manufacture, sell, and repair e-bikes. New brand names of bike manufacturers have emerged that didn't exist 5 or 10 years ago. One of the largest and most successful of these new e-bike-only companies is Pedego Electric Bikes. You can read Pedego's story and about the firm's co-founder and CEO in the Rider Profile that follows this chapter. 👓

Don DiCostanzo
Co-Founder and CEO, Pedego Electric Bikes

How a Hill Helped Launch America's
Largest Retail E-Bike Company

"I'm not a cyclist, I'm an electric bike rider, and there's a big difference."

Don DiCostanzo, Co-Founder & CEO, Pedego Electric Bikes. Used per permission of Pedego Electric Bikes

Living at the top of a hill is what originally piqued Don DiCostanzo's interest in electric bikes. That interest has since blossomed into Pedego Electric Bikes, the largest e-bike retailer in North America, of which he is co-founder and chief executive officer.

"I lived at the top of the hill, and I loved to ride my bike down the hill to the beach, but I hated going back up that hill," Don said in an interview for this book. "So consequently, I would go to my garage, and I'd see my car and I'd see my bike, and I'd pick the car because I'd think about that hill."

At a time when e-bikes were not yet well known, Don looked online and bought an electric bike so he could conquer that hill. "It was a terrible bike, but it got me up the hill, so I said there's something to this. I bought seven more electric bikes in the next few months. I had them in my garage. It was a hobby."

When friends discovered Don's bikes, they wanted one too. So in 2007 Don opened an electric bike shop (called Z-Clips) in Newport Beach, California, and quickly became the largest electric bike retailer in the U.S.

"It was an instant success. I quickly figured out that electric bikes was where it was at, but nobody made a decent one, so I ended up making my own."

The start of Pedego Electric Bikes

Disappointed by the poor quality of the e-bikes available at that time, in 2008 Don co-founded Pedego Electric Bikes, determined to manufacture and sell a better-quality e-bike that would appeal to the average consumer.

"In that one-year laboratory (owning the Newport Beach store), I learned what customers want. I learned they want two things. The women want to know what colors the bikes come in and the men want to know how fast they will go and how far they will go. I built bikes based on those three questions - how fast they will go, how far they will go, and what colors they come in."

Today, Pedego has nearly 200 retail stores and a dedicated customer base. The private Pedego Owners Group on Facebook has more than 10,000 members and new posts every day. Stores often sponsor customer-appreciation events and host group rides for owners and their friends.

Don said his goal for Pedego is to be the one brand the public associates first with e-bikes, like Harley-Davidson is for motorcycles or Starbucks for coffee shops.

Targeting senior adults and the non-cycling crowd

From the beginning, Don said Pedego has targeted the average consumer, not the hard-core cyclists that most local bike shops have traditionally catered to.

"I'm not a cyclist, I'm an electric bike rider, and there's a big difference. I've never been a competitive cyclist. I'm like most of our customers and most of the seniors in the world. Pedego has always been focused on the people who don't ride bikes, who aren't riding bikes because of the four-letter word 'hill' or the four-letter word called 'wind.' Those are the two things that keep people from riding bikes as they get older."

Pedego caters to the Baby Boomer generation, both in the bikes they build and in the customer experience they receive in the stores.

"There's a younger generation beginning to buy our bikes, but our sweet spot is still the aging Baby Boomer, people moving into retirement and looking for something to do, and the best part is the social element. They like to ride together."

While the typical Pedego e-bike customer is in his or her late 50s, Don said they have had numerous customers in their 80s and even some in their 90s.

"We've got a guy in Florida who is already on his second (Pedego) bike. He's 80-some-odd-years-old, lives in Naples, and rode his first Pedego 38,000 miles. This guy gets up every morning and rides 50 miles a day. That's his recreation; that's his life."

Why E-Bike Cycling Appeals To Baby Boomers

Bicycling, especially nowadays with e-bikes, is an activity that appeals to senior adults on many levels, Don said.

"It (cycling) is a non-impact event. Cycling is one of the best exercises you can do. Swimming is probably number one, cycling is number two. I do both. I swim virtually every day, and I cycle virtually every day.

"The second is it's enjoyable. People enjoy riding their bikes, and people are not going to do an exercise unless they enjoy it.

"The third thing is it's something you can do in a group, or you can do it by yourself. If you go to the gym, it's kinda by yourself, and if you swim, it's really by yourself, it's a one-man sport.

"The fourth thing is it's also social. You can ride down to Starbucks.

"The fifth thing is you can use it for transportation. You can go to the post office, you can go to the grocery store. People like to use their bikes for utilitarian reasons.

"I think the most important reason is that it's fun. Everybody enjoys it. It's fun, you get exercise, it's social."

Don is a personal testimony to the benefits senior adults can receive from riding e-bikes.

"I'm 63 years old and have lost 20 pounds. I'm in the best physical shape I've ever been in my life. I have unbelievable balance, even though I was a clumsy person my whole life. Today, I'm not clumsy at all. My reaction time has improved. It's unbelievable. When you talk with the doctors, they say of course it (cycling) would improve balance. When you're riding a bike, you're constantly balancing. All of the things in your physiology that are designed to help you with balance are being played every second you are on the bike."

Don said he credits his weight loss to his exercising and practicing good nutrition.

Behind the scenes, Don has been a strong advocate within the e-bike industry and with regulators for allowing throttles on e-bikes. He believes a throttle is especially helpful for older riders because it helps them take off from a dead start and to move up hills with less effort. It helps them to catch up when falling behind in a riding group. For some seniors with certain health concerns and disabilities, a throttle can make the difference between getting to be outdoors and riding or being sidelined and stuck indoors.

He described the feeling of using a throttle on an e-bike to being akin to "a magic carpet ride."

"The throttle is a game changer. Nobody should buy an electric bike without a throttle."

Rent Before You Buy

Don's advice to consumers is to first rent an e-bike, try it out, before buying it.

"Go rent. Try them all out. Try them for size, try them for comfort. When you get an e-bike, it's like buying a pair of shoes. When you get an uncomfortable pair of shoes, you're not going to wear them. A bike is a huge investment, so why wouldn't you take it for a test drive? Would you buy a car without taking it for a test drive? Everybody has different dimensions, different arm lengths and leg lengths. Everybody's different. One size (bike) doesn't fit all." 👓

CHAPTER 7

Choosing a Senior-Friendly E-Bike, Part 2

"I love my e-bike! It's the only way I can ride now with the disaster that is my right knee. I'm so glad I don't have to give up biking! Oh, and mine also folds and fits in the back of my Outback. Winning all around!"

– *Senior cyclist quoted on Facebook*

"Went 42 miles first time out at 68 years of age. While I can and like to ride my road bike, for long distance, an e-bike can't be beat."

– *Senior cyclist quoted on Facebook*

In Chapter 6, **I began the discussion of what to look for** when buying an e-bike and discussed the importance of knowing how you plan to use the bike. There is no one "best" e-bike style for all riders and all occasions. I weighed the pros and cons of buying from a local bike shop versus buying online. I looked at a realistic budget for buying an e-bike, so you don't make the mistake of shopping based merely on the lowest price. By the end of this chapter, you should be well equipped to begin your search for an e-bike, whether it's your first one or you are ready to expand or upgrade your e-bike collection. Let's start with some guidance about e-bike brands.

Which Brand Should I Buy?

Which brand of e-bike to buy is a question often asked on social media cycling forums. It's no wonder newcomers to the e-bike scene are often confused about brands. The number of new brands has exploded in recent years. In the U.S. alone, there are an estimated 400 brands of e-bikes competing for the public's attention. Unlike some consumer products like cellphones or soft drinks, there are no two or three well-known brands that strongly dominate the e-bike market, at least not yet.

Like in any consumer product, not all e-bikes are made with equal quality. You want to buy a bike that will meet your needs and give you years of safe and reasonably trouble-free service. So which brand of e-bike should you buy?

Perhaps it is a testimony to the generally good quality of most e-bikes being sold in North America today that most respondents on social media are quick to recommend whatever brand they happen to own. In other words, most seniors are happy enough with the brand they bought, whether it was bought from a local bike shop or purchased online, and whether it cost $1,500 or $5,000.

That's not to say there aren't real quality differences among brands and at different price points. You will no doubt have a happier experience if you choose wisely and can afford to buy a better-quality e-bike. Even so, there is no agreement among e-cycling enthusiasts as to which brand is "best." Nor will I dare to be presumptuous enough to try to tell you which brand of e-bike to buy. Instead, in this chapter, I will talk about types (styles) of e-bikes most popular with senior cyclists and how to narrow your choice to get the e-bike that best fits your needs.

Before leaving the question about brands, however, here are some general guidelines that may prove helpful in your search. The choice of e-bikes on the market today is overwhelming and still expanding.

It's a lucrative market and plenty of companies and entrepreneurs are eager to capture even a small slice of it.

So how do you select the brand of e-bike that is right for you? These questions will help you make a wiser choice:

Does the company have a retail presence in your country? As discussed in Chapter 6, buying through a local bike shop has many advantages. You can test ride bikes before purchasing, the store will be available for fitting you to your new bike and answering your questions, and the store will provide after-sale service and warranty work. For the average senior cyclist, these benefits are a big plus. In addition, while buying an e-bike through a local store is no guarantee that you will always purchase a high-quality bike, it is a safe generalization to say that dealers carry bikes that are at least of average quality, if not better. Nearly all of the truly high-end e-bikes are sold through dealers, not online. Dealers typically won't carry the lower-end products that are more likely to cause trouble for them and their customers. It's a positive sign if the brand of e-bike you are considering is being sold through local bike shops in your country.

Does the company have ANY presence in your country or region? Many smaller brands have nothing more than a post office box presence in major markets in which they are attempting to sell bikes. It may be an Asian brand, for instance, seeking to grab some quick market share in North America or the EU but with no personnel or offices on either continent. They may give their bikes a local-sounding name and sell them through online sites like Amazon or market directly to consumers on social media. Buying an e-bike from such a company can be problematic. If you need parts a year or two from now to repair your e-bike, you may be out of luck. You may be unable to contact anyone at the company who speaks your language to ask questions or get warranty work. On an investment of this size, it's not worth the risk.

How long has the company been selling e-bikes? You're safer sticking with brands that have some history. Narrow your search to companies with a minimum of five years (preferably more) in the e-bike business.

Is the company a significant player in the e-bike industry? The top 25 or so e-bike companies in a given market (North America, the UK, or the European Union, for instance) account for the vast majority of all sales. While this doesn't necessarily mean their bikes are better quality than some of the smaller firms, they must be doing something right to gain that level of success. Besides, larger companies have the resources to continually innovate and improve their products, and to offer a superior customer experience. Larger companies are more likely to stand behind their warranties. They have staying power in the industry. There are some fine smaller specialty firms catering to unique niches of the e-bike market, but as a general rule the average senior cyclist will be better served by sticking with one of the larger, more established e-bike companies. It's a big investment, so why not buy from a successful company versus a start-up?

Where was the e-bike manufactured? Actually, this is a trick question. Don't fret too much over the country of origin of your e-bike. The reality is that on a worldwide basis more than 80 percent of ALL e-bikes are manufactured in China, Taiwan, or elsewhere in Southeast Asia. The EU is next in terms of e-bike manufacturing, with North American companies (U.S. and Canada) coming in third. Even if you buy a bike from a U.S.-based company, that is no assurance that it was "made" in the United States. Don't be fooled by thinking you are buying a bike made in your country just because the brand is a familiar one and sounds local. Raleigh and Schwinn, for instance, two well-known brands with U.S. and UK roots, manufacture most of their bikes in Taiwan. Many bike brands will order e-bikes from Asian manufacturers that meet their design, quality, and component specifications, and then add their brand label. Other companies will buy component parts (motors, frames, batteries, brake assemblies, gear systems, etc.) from Asia and do assembly or final assembly inside the United States, Canada, or Europe. The country of origin of your bike (or its component parts) should not be a major factor in deciding which e-bike to buy.

Styles of e-bikes best suited for senior riders

While some of the more athletically inclined or thrill-seeking senior adults will favor performance-oriented road bikes or mountain bikes, most of us at this age want a bicycle that is comfortable, reliable, and easy to use.

Here are some popular styles of e-bikes suitable for the majority of senior adults:

The Pedego Comfort Cruiser, Step-Thru Model. Photo Used With Permission, ©2021, Pedego Electric Bikes

Step-through bikes: A step-through bike isn't so much a type of bike as it is a design feature. Do you remember the bikes we rode years ago that had those high top frame bars that we had to swing our legs over to mount the bike? Back in the day, those were called "boys bikes" while bikes with a lower frame bar were referred to as "girls bikes." Things have changed. At our more advanced ages, swinging a leg over that top bar isn't as easy as it once was. Due to hip or lower-back issues, step-through bikes are favored by many seniors, both men and women. Step-through bikes today are gender-neutral and no longer carry the "girls' bike" stigma.

Step-through (or "low step") bikes come in a choice of sizes, with 20, 24, or 26 inch tires. Shorter riders may feel more comfortable on a smaller-size e-bike. Step-through bikes are also considered safer for senior riders. Many accidents happen while riders are trying to mount or dismount from their bikes; step-through bikes eliminate this problem. Plus, if you need to jump off the bike quickly for one reason or another, that's much easier to do on a step-through bike.

The Pedego Element Fat Tire Electric Bike. Used With Permission, ©2021, Pedego Electric Bikes

Fat-tire bikes: Bike tires come in a variety of widths. Road (racing-style) bikes, designed for minimal road friction and fast speeds, are often less than one inch wide. While great for athletes, thin tires are not usually best for seniors. They provide a harder ride, less stability, and if you are unfortunate enough to catch these thin tires just right in a road grate, you are probably going to go airborne over the handlebars and sustain some serious injuries. Your more typical cruiser-style bikes (see description below), come with wider tires, usually 2.0 to 2.5 inches. These tires provide a more comfortable ride.

A newer and increasingly popular category of e-bike is called "fat-tire bikes" or just "fat bikes." These bikes sport wide tires in widths of 3.0 to 5.0 inches. Many seniors favor these sizes because of the cushiony-smooth ride and stability. Plus, fat-tire bikes can go off-road more easily, riding with no problem through dirt, gravel, and sand. That makes them popular with RVers and other campers. On a traditional bike, tires of this width would be hard to pedal, but with electric power they are no problem. One drawback of fatter tires is the extra weight they add to an already-heavy e-bike. Fat tires are commonly adapted to cruiser bikes and small foldable bikes, both of which are popular styles with Baby Boomers.

The Pedego Cruiser. Photo Used With Permission, ©2021, Pedego Electric Bikes

Cruiser bikes: Also known as "comfort bikes," cruisers put riders in a more upright position, not bent over the handlebars. This is the most popular bike style for Baby Boomers. These e-bikes feature wider, cushioned seats that are easier on aging bodies. Cruiser bikes also have wider tires (2.0 to 2.5 inch) that improve control, balance and ride. Cruiser e-bikes will typically include hand brakes and a selection of from 3 to 14 gears, which makes riding up hills easier. While the standard, full-size 26-inch bike size is suitable for most adults, those of shorter stature may want to ask about 24-inch cruiser-style bikes. Some brands also offer a larger 29-inch tire cruiser bike for taller riders. Test ride various sizes and models before choosing the one that's best for you. Getting the right fit is extremely important.

Cruisers are great for riding longer distances due to their comfort, power, and smoothness. Many senior cyclists who enjoy riding long-distance bike trails or go on multi-day bike trips favor cruiser-style e-bikes. They are also capable of carrying heavier riders and added cargo loads.

Cruiser e-bikes are often fully decked out with front and rear fenders, bells, lights, rear luggage racks (or baskets). They make great all-purpose bikes that are easy to ride. One drawback of the cruiser-style bike is its weight. These are among the heaviest of all e-bikes, especially if equipped with fat tires and all accessories. The RadRover 5, one of the best-selling e-bikes in North America, weighs 69 pounds, which can make lifting and transporting the bike difficult for some senior adults.

Domane+ ALR Road e-Bike.
©2021, Trek Bicycle Corporation

Road bikes: Road bikes are traditionally thought of as "racing bikes" designed for athletes, with long-slung handlebars, thin tires and skinny seats. Today, however, there are many variations of the road bike designed to make them better suited to casual riders and more comfortable to ride, while maintaining the basic road-bike design and performance.

If you are accustomed to road bikes but realize that with age you are struggling more to maintain your speed or keep up with younger buddies in your bike club, then you should take a look at an electric version of the classic road bike. Top-end brands offer sleek, lightweight, stylish road bikes that will help you stay in the game longer and enjoy it more. This is not the type of e-bike that most senior adults will prefer, but road bikes do have a loyal following, even among the 55+ demographic. Expect to pay toward the higher end of the range for a quality road e-bike, between $3,000 and $6,000.

Powerfly FS 4 Mountain e-Bike.
©2021, Trek Bicycle Corporation

Mountain bikes: Like road bikes, mountain bikes are not a style that appeals to most senior adults. Even so, there is a dedicated group of seniors, mainly men, who are physically fit and still love the adrenalin rush that mountain biking provides. Mountain bikers ride off-road on narrow dirt trails, many of which offer challenging, twisty routes, with hills to climb, rocks to avoid, and obstacles to jump. It is a more dangerous sport, but mountain bike enthusiasts swear by it. Riders tend to wear proper armor to protect themselves, offsetting some of the additional risk. For seniors who wish to pursue mountain biking, the good news is that an increasing number of mountain bikes now come with electric power. This makes it more feasible for older adults to continue to pursue the sport and ride longer per day, thanks to e-bike technology.

Premium II Low Step Folding e-Bike. Photo Used With Permission, ©2021, Magnum Electric Bikes

Foldable e-bikes: An increasingly popular bike style for senior adults is the foldable electric bike. While they come in tire sizes from 16 to 26 inches, the most popular size is the foldable bike with 20-inch tires. On a traditional bike, smaller tires might make pedaling harder, but on an e-bike you won't notice any difference.

These smaller bikes are especially popular with RV owners because of how portable they are. They fit easily inside an RV or in the back of an SUV or minivan. You don't need a bike rack to transport a small foldable bike. Campers say the bikes come in handy as a means of transportation within the campground and to nearby stores, especially if your RV is a motorhome or cab-style RV (Class A, B, or C) where you don't have a separate vehicle to drive.

Small foldable e-bikes open up many new opportunities for senior travelers. Since they are carried inside your vehicle and not hanging from the back on a rack, you won't have to lug them into your hotel at night or worry as much about them being stolen or exposed to rain and bad weather. Plus, you can ship these bikes more easily by airplane, taking them with you on trips. You can buy both soft and hard-case bags designed to carry foldable e-bikes for travel purposes. You can also carry small foldable bikes on all sorts of public transportation — trains, buses, even ferries. Imagine the opportunities that can open up for senior travelers eager to explore new countryside or urban areas.

Another plus of the smaller size, foldable e-bike is if you are traveling with a friend who doesn't have a trailer hitch or e-bike rack on his car. You can simply put the folded bike in the trunk. A small, foldable e-bike can also be useful if you get stranded far from your car while riding on a bike trail or country roads. Almost any motorist can give you a lift into town or back to your car, tossing your "folder" bike into the car's trunk.

When buying a small foldable e-bike, select one with tire widths that match your riding needs. This is a popular size bike for fat tires, as described above. If you are a camper who plans to ride through the woods, or if you plan to ride your bike often at the beach or in soft sand, then fat tires will be a plus. If you will primarily ride on paved trails and neighborhood roads, then you won't benefit from fat tires. Tires in the 2.25 to 3.0 inch range are a good compromise size for most senior e-bikers.

Canadian Mike Duhaime (at left), 60, of Cornwall, Ontario, is a fan of 20-inch e-bikes. "As my third e-bike, the smaller fat (tire) bike with 20-inch wheels is definitely safer, easier to corner, fits between trail posts better, and is just handier."

Mike and his wife are fortunate enough to live along a 35-mile bike trail along the St. Lawrence River that they ride nearly every day when weather permits. They have also taken small foldable e-bikes on bike trips to ride on trails in Quebec.

Another benefit of the 20-inch e-bike, according to Mike, is the added safety. The smaller size and step-through design common on many foldable bikes makes them more ideally suited for seniors.

Smaller e-bikes are also safer because they maneuver better. "You can turn on a dime," Mike said, noting that the tighter turning is especially beneficial on trails with sharp curves. A smaller bike, he said, can make the difference between successfully navigating a turn and falling off the bike while attempting to turn.

Like cruiser e-bikes, 20-inch foldable e-bikes often come with fenders, a bell, and front-and-rear lights. They are versatile bikes that can satisfy a wide range of consumers. They are not considered the best choice if your main goal is to regularly engage in longer-distance rides, let's say in excess of 20 miles per day. A larger cruiser (or road bike) is going to be more comfortable for this purpose. With that said, plenty of seniors use small "folders" for long-distance rides and seem pleased with their experience. See the Rider Profile following this chapter for one senior cyclist's experience with riding a 20-inch foldable bike for longer distances.

When shopping for a foldable e-bike, it's especially important to buy a good-quality brand. Cheaper foldable bikes have been known to suffer from frame integrity issues and may have less effective or durable folding mechanisms. As you might expect, the folding hinge on an e-bike is a critically important component. The better bike brands have well-engineered folding mechanisms that should provide a solid feel and last for the longer run. Some inexpensive brands of folding bikes are also underpowered and won't handle hills well.

Pathfinder 500 W Non-Folding Small e-Bike.
Photo Used With Permission,
©2021, Magnum Electric Bikes

Non-foldable small bikes: If you like the idea of a smaller-size e-bike, with or without fat tires, but don't need it to fold up, there are plenty of 20-inch e-bikes on the market that offer all of the advantages mentioned above in terms of being easy to maneuver and control. These e-bikes come in a wide range of styles and are also popular with Baby Boomers.

An interesting variation of this small-size bike is the so-called ***cargo e-bike,*** a muscular version of a small e-bike that is built to carry heavier loads, often with large front and/or rear racks or baskets. Some businesses in urban areas use cargo bikes for deliveries. These bikes are heavy, but are great for carrying cargo as well as general riding.

For seniors who want a great bike to take to the supermarket and don't need to transport the bike on the car to trails, a 20-inch cargo e-bike may be worth a look. Some cargo bikes also come in a larger frame size with 24-inch tires. By the way, cargo bikes are great for carrying small grandchildren. Some brands have specially made seating, foot rests, and bracing for carrying one or two small children.

Trikes: Another popular style of e-bike for Baby Boomers these days is the three-wheel tricycle. I will discuss them in the next chapter.

Want to know what it's like to ride a 20-inch bike? Read the interesting Rider Profile on the next page for one senior cyclist's perspective. 👓

Christine McArthur

*Touring the National Parks with a
20-inch Foldable E-Bike*

"You will find things on an e-bike that you just aren't going to see driving through a neighborhood (in a car)."

Christine McArthur, 68, likes to have a destination in mind when she rides her e-bike, even if it's just stopping at Starbucks or going for a pizza.

"It gives you a reason to be on your bike, aside from exercise," said Christine, who lives in Las Vegas.

She has now set her sights on a much more challenging destination: touring all of the national parks in the lower 48 states on her e-bike, or at least all the ones she hasn't already visited.

"I need a challenge and a sense of purpose," Christine said.

Traveling in her RV and carrying her e-bike,

Christine's goal is to visit as many national parks as possible during the year ahead. Already she's visited Zion and Bryce National Parks in Utah, among others.

Christine bought her first e-bike in 2018, and is now on her second one, a Bagi Bike Fat Tire B10, a small folding e-bike with fat (four-inch-width) tires.

"I treat this bike like most people treat their pets," Christine said, noting that many of her friends, especially her camping friends, have bought e-bikes after test-riding hers and seeing how much she enjoys it.

"A lot of people have never tried an e-bike, so I let them try mine. I don't care if they buy my bike (brand) because you've got to buy the bike that's right for you."

Even for senior adults who haven't ridden a bike in years, the sense of pleasure once they rediscover cycling is almost universal.

"I have younger friends who haven't been on a bike in years. Once they get on an e-bike, it's like it turns back time. My friend Donna and I, we feel like little kids. The sense of freedom is hard to beat."

When weather and work allow it, Christine is on her bike most days of the week. Her goal is to ride 100 miles per week, typically averaging 20 to 27 miles per ride.

An e-bike has been especially helpful for Christine because she lives in a hilly area.

"I live 3,000 feet above sea level. When I go out my gate, I have to go up another 1,000 feet to get to the trail. I could never do that on a regular bike."

Whether riding around the neighborhood or touring a majestic national park, Christine says her e-bike gives her a far better vantage point to observe and appreciate the world around her compared with driving a car.

"You will find things on an e-bike that you just aren't going to see driving through a neighborhood (in a car). I've found cute little parks here in Las Vegas that I never knew existed, and I have lived here 11 years.

"It's a sense of discovery." 👓

Is Life Better on Three Wheels? Electric Trikes Gain in Popularity with Seniors

"I am disabled. In fact, I ride my wheelchair to my trike and wife helps me transfer from the wheelchair to my trike. I ride about 2,000 miles per year and enjoy it a lot ... My trike has been a big-time life changer for me."

– Senior cyclist quoted on Facebook

"That pure power is like someone pushing you. It's like a magic carpet feeling. You will smile like you've had a sensation like you've never had before."

– Jason Kraft, CEO, Electric Bike Technologies

If you think "adult tricycles" aren't cool enough for you as a Baby Boomer to ride, maybe it's time to think again. Trike designs are far sleeker today than those slow, old-fashioned models that previous generations rode. Plus, when you add an electric motor to a trike, you've got a fast, versatile machine that will turn heads when you zoom by.

"You can ride three wheels and be cool at the same time," said Jason Kraft, CEO of Electric Bike Technologies[40], one of America's largest sellers of electric trikes.

E-trikes are one of the most fun and versatile vehicles available today for seniors. They provide a safer alternative to the traditional two-wheel bicycle and open up opportunities for outdoor exercise and exploration for a broader range of senior adults, including those with less strength and stamina, poor balance, or mobility limitations.

David Clayton, a senior-adult cyclist who lives in Ocala, Florida, loves his e-trike so much that he penned a poem about it. He was kind enough to let us share it with you.

Trikes: No More Fear of Falling

Just a recumbent trike named Tricky.
She can ride up North or whistle Dixie.
Doesn't matter what mood I'm in
As I turn those pedals I start to grin.
Sites and scenes pass on by
Yes, she's the apple of my eye.
Fat tires on a wet sandy beach,
Paradise lies within our reach.
So much fun it just isn't fair,
Riding on the perfect beach chair.
We're not that fast but can't you see,
We can ride all day my trike and me.

One of the biggest concerns of many seniors who are considering buying an e-bike is the fear of falling. Their friends are buying e-bikes and they really want to join the fun, but this fear holds them back. Many seniors say they no longer have as keen a sense of balance and coordination.

Compounding this concern is the fact that falls at our more advanced ages can result in more serious injuries. A broken bone at age 75 can be far more serious than a broken bone at age 25.

Some people never mastered the art of balancing themselves on a two-wheel bike, even as a child, and if they rode at all, they did so in a wobbly manner and with a lack of confidence. For these people, the idea of riding a two-wheel bike again, especially with a motor that will propel them at even higher speeds, is scary indeed.

Today's adult-size tricycles solve this problem. You don't have to balance yourself on a three-wheel trike, so a lack of coordination is not a barrier. You don't have to worry about stopping and putting your feet down at every intersection and then trying to get the bike moving again without losing your balance. These are real worries for some seniors on two-wheel bikes.

Falling from a trike is not likely, but even if you do fall, you are much closer to the ground, significantly reducing the impact. That's not to say tricycles are accident-free. You can tip over a trike by turning too sharply or too fast in a curve or trying to ride on sloped terrain, but the chances of having an accident on a trike are far less than on a two-wheel bike. Of course, whether riding on two wheels or three, you still have to observe traffic laws and watch out for other cyclists, road hazards, pedestrians, and motorists.

Trikes Can Meet Seniors' Everyday Transportation Needs

Adult-size trikes are widely used for recreation, riding on trails, and for exercise, just like two-wheel bikes. Beyond those uses, however, trikes are more capable than their two-wheel cousins at meeting senior adults' everyday transportation needs. Trikes can serve as a good car substitute or as a "second car" that is perfect for running short errands.

If you are blessed to live in an area with good cycling infrastructure such as bike trails and streets with bike lanes, it is easy to use a trike to buy groceries at the supermarket, pick up prescriptions at the corner pharmacy, or buy a fast-food meal. One of the big advantages of a trike is its ability to carry cargo and do so safely. Many trikes come with large baskets that can hold at least a couple of bags of groceries. It is safer to carry cargo on a trike versus a bike since riding with packages on a trike won't throw off your balance or upset the vehicle's weight distribution.

Do you like to take your dog with you wherever you go? You can easily carry your small furry friends with you on your trike. Most dogs love the open-air feel of cycling. Imagine cycling with your pooch and visiting the local dog park, where you can visit with friends while giving your pet a chance to exercise and socialize.

Thanks to the extra cargo room and better balancing, trikes are also ideal if you need to carry health-related supplies with you, such as an oxygen machine or walking aids.

Trikes, especially electric-powered trikes, can even make participating in certain outdoor hobbies more doable and more enjoyable.

"If you're a bird watcher, you don't want to be putting the (two wheel) bike down all the time and worrying about the kickstand and whatever. You want something that can carry your gear and you can relax," said Jason Kraft, CEO of Electric Bike Technologies[41] (left). "Maybe you're not in the best of shape to do your bird-watching. You're going out on the trail and maybe you could only pedal two miles, but with this (electric) trike, you've got at least a 10-mile range. You can see a lot more cranes in 10 miles, and you can do it in comfort, with your gear in the back."

Jason said he's aware of other customers who use their e-trikes for fishing and even hunting. One of his company's subsidiaries, ElectricTrike.com, is a popular online retailer of e-trikes.

Why You Should Electrify Your Trike

Plenty of cyclists enjoy riding non-electric, traditional adult trikes. More power to them (pun intended) but if your personal experience in the past with traditional trikes is anything like mine, you know they can have their shortcomings. Many non-electric trikes can be slow and hard to pedal. That's because trikes are heavier than bikes and create more drag or friction since they have three tires on the ground, not two. **If you have hills to ride, a traditional trike is not your friend.**

If you are a senior adult and considering buying a trike, you will likely want one with an electric motor. Electrifying a trike makes a world of difference. Rather than dreading the difficulty of pedaling, you will look forward to each and every ride. You will easily conquer hills and cover longer distances. Riding will be fun again.

In an interview for this book, Jason described the benefits of adding electric power: "You have to pedal all the time on a regular bike if you want it to move. When you are on an electric bike, you can pedal if you'd like to, you can get as much exercise as you'd like to, but if you want to, you can use pure power only as well. That pure power is like someone pushing you. It's like a magic carpet feeling. You will smile like you've had a sensation like you've never had before. It's pure propulsion with no noise and no smell and no heat, where you just turn a piece of plastic and it thrusts the trike forward. It's magical. For seniors who maybe can't ride as far as they used to, it enables them to ride farther, ride more, and ride easier if they choose to."

Popular Types of E-Trikes

Electric-powered trikes come in a variety of designs. As with bikes, you will ideally want to try out a few at bike shops and/or talk with friends who already own trikes to learn what is best for you. Unfortunately, many bike shops have few, if any, e-trikes to choose from, which means it may be more likely you will have to consider buying your e-trike online. Still, you may want to check first with local shops to see what they offer.

Let's look at some of the more common types of trikes.

Photo used by permission of electrictrike.com

Recumbents: Recumbent trikes sport a sleek design, with a riding position that is lower to the ground. With a recumbent, you sit in a semi-reclining position with your legs in front of you. This position is more comfortable and less tiring. Many recumbents have wider seats, often with back support. Unlike some of the heavier, more traditional trikes, many recumbents offer speed and performance that will satisfy experienced cyclists.

Most recumbents feature a different steering system than other bikes and trikes. Rather than the typical handlebars, recumbent trikes often have under-seat steering, with small handlebars on both sides of the trike. This puts your hands in a more natural, relaxed position, without resting your weight on your wrists and hands. Some recumbents have more traditional, higher handlebars, which is an easier transition for many seniors who are coming from a history of riding bicycles.

As with e-bikes, some e-trikes come in a folding design. This is a helpful feature if you need to carry your recumbent e-trike with you in an RV, SUV, minivan or pickup truck. Folding is also helpful if you need to store your e-trike inside your apartment or house.

Photo used by permission of electrictrike.com

Tadpole vs. Delta: Recumbents come in two frame styles - Tadpoles and Delta. Tadpole trikes (top left) have two wheels in the front and only one in the back, whereas Delta trikes (bottom left) offer two wheels in the rear and one in the front.

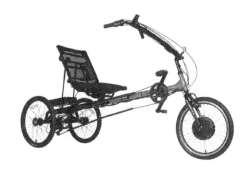

Photo used by permission of electrictrike.com

There are pros and cons for both styles. Tadpole trikes sit very low to the ground and are known for maneuvering well and attaining higher speeds. Delta trikes sit higher off the ground (but not as high as traditional adult trikes) and can make tighter turns. Delta trikes are easier to get off and on because they have a higher sitting position. This makes them appealing to many seniors. At the same time, the higher sitting position means Delta trikes are somewhat easier to tip over, but this is not a common occurrence. Cyclists who watch their speed, especially in turns, and drive safely are unlikely to tip over their recumbent trike, regardless of which style trike they own.

Photo used by permission of electrictrike.com

Adult Trikes: Modern variations of the traditional "adult trike" design are also popular with seniors. These e-trikes offer a higher sitting position that is very easy to mount and dismount. The higher sitting position also offers a better view of the road and visibility to motorists.

Like a Delta-style recumbent trike, traditional trikes usually feature two wheels in the rear, with a large basket between them, and one wheel in the front. Handlebars resemble a traditional bicycle's handlebars, so adjusting to the riding style is easier. These trikes may be heavier and slower than some of the sleeker recumbent models, but they offer a comfortable, predictable ride with great versatility for carrying cargo. When you add electric technology, even these trikes have no problem climbing hills and letting you cruise at a comfortable speed, with or without pedaling (if equipped with a throttle). These trikes are popular in many 55+ communities and are useful for running errands to stores or carrying pets.

Specialty Trikes: Some e-trikes are specially designed with seniors in mind, especially seniors with physical limitations or anyone who just wants a safe, easy-to-operate machine and isn't concerned about cycling at higher speeds or for extra-long distances at a time.

An example of this style of specialty e-trikes is the Liberty Electric[42] Mobility Tricycle, which has found a much wider audience than the original target group of seniors with reduced strength and stamina or living in assisted living communities. It has been a success story for Jason Kraft's Electric Bike

Photo used by permission of libertytrike.com

Technologies[43] and has a loyal following. Liberty Trike owners have their own Facebook group page with 3,000 members.

Like a traditional trike, the Liberty Trike has an upright sitting position, a step-through design for easy mounting, a comfortable seat, and handlebars. You can choose to pedal for exercise or use the throttle. With a 750-watt motor, the Liberty Trike can cruise smoothly on level ground and manage most hills. Unlike most other e-bikes and e-trikes, you can go in reverse, helping riders back into tight spaces.

Specialty e-trikes like the Liberty Trike aren't as fast as recumbent electric trikes and don't have as long a cruising range. The Liberty Trike has a maximum speed of 12 mph and a range of 8 to 20 miles per charge. That's less than other styles of e-trikes but more than enough for most of the seniors who purchase these trikes.

Jason said Liberty Trikes are often viewed as a cooler, more fun alternative to using a mobility scooter.

"It's life-changing. The coolest thing is it's not like a mobility scooter. It's not slow and it doesn't have that negative connotation of somebody in a mobility scooter. Besides that, a mobility scooter gives you zero exercise. We call Liberty Trikes 'active mobility' because you get to exercise if you want to.

"Seniors just love it. It changes their lives. It allows them to go at a reasonable speed for an adult."

Jason said Liberty Trikes make senior buyers feel better about their situation than the alternative of driving a mobility scooter.

"Baby Boomers look at mobility scooters and they think, 'OK, last step before the coffin,' and they don't want to get in one of those things. It's demoralizing. They've gone through seeing their parents get on them (mobility scooters) and die a couple of years later as a heavy person. That's a terrible way to be."

Nowadays, the Liberty Trike and similar models from other trike brands can be seen cruising on bike trails, taking riders on errands to nearby stores, and buzzing around campgrounds. The trikes fold, making them easy to transport in an RV, SUV, or minivan. Seniors even ride them inside many supermarkets, superstores, and other stores, just like a mobility scooter.

In the Rider Profile following this chapter, you can read one senior's story of how a Liberty Trike helped her gain greater mobility and overcome her medical disabilities.

Drawbacks

Electric trikes are the best solution for some seniors. E-trike owners tend to be very pleased with their bikes. At the same time, e-trikes do have some unique drawbacks compared with e-bikes. If considering whether to buy an e-trike, be aware of these issues:

Heavier weight: Electric trikes are heavier than most e-bikes. This makes them harder to lift and handle for many seniors.

Harder to transport: E-trikes are also bulky. If you only plan to ride it around your neighborhood, town, or on nearby trails you can access from home, then transporting your e-trike is not an issue. On the other hand, if you dream of carrying your trike with you on trips or to ride on trails across town or across the country, then you will need to come up with a plan for how to transport it. Many trailer-hitch-mounted e-bike racks will not accommodate trikes, or will require special adaptors. If you wish to carry your trike inside your vehicle, you may find it is too large. There are, however, workable solutions. My wife owns an e-trike (and loves it). It fits nicely inside our minivan, with the second and third rows of seats down. Another solution is to buy an e-trike that is foldable. If you have two e-trikes in the family, you could also consider buying (or renting) a small enclosed trailer to haul behind your car.

Limited range: While not true of every e-trike, most of them will not travel as far per battery charge as a comparable e-bike, due to their extra weight and road friction. The range may be more than adequate for your needs, but if you plan to use your trike for longer-distance rides, this may be a consideration. One solution to this is to buy a second battery for use on longer rides. Unlike on a bike, on a trike there is ample room for carrying an extra battery.

Despite these challenges, electric-powered trikes can be a great choice for many seniors. They are fun to ride and relatively safe. If you have any health limitations or reservations about riding a two-wheel bike, or just prefer the safety and comfort of riding on a more stable three-wheel machine, then check out the ever-expanding variety of e-trikes available today. 👓

Julie Hancock Austad

*How Her Trike Helped Her Overcome a Disability
and Break Free of Isolation*

"Your whole demeanor changes when you can get out of your
house and just go around the block and around city streets."

Before buying an electric trike, Julie Hancock Austad said she
had not been inside a grocery store for 20 years. She suffers from
degenerative joint disease, so walking anywhere farther than the
mailbox was out of the question.

Julie's life changed in dramatic fashion after she took her first ride on a Liberty Trike, a small electric trike popular with people with mobility issues because owners can ride their Liberty Trikes into stores.

"I took it out for a ride and said this feels pretty good," said Julie, 66, who lives in Everett, Washington. "I rode for an hour. I came back and said this is wonderful."

Julie not only bought a Liberty Trike, but it wasn't long before her husband did too. In the three years since then, Frank and Julie have taken their trikes not only inside grocery stores but around the country when they travel.

"We rode them all over Las Vegas, even inside a casino," Julie said. "It's been a real lifesaver. I can actually get out and see things."

The couple carries their trikes with them when they travel in their motor home. When they reach a campground, they use their trikes to get around, even taking them to nearby stores. Their Liberty Trikes have accompanied them to Gettysburg, Pennsylvania, Winslow, Arizona, and Branson, Missouri, among other places.

Electric trikes have opened up a whole new world for people with mobility disabilities like Julie. Not only do they gain a form of exercise, but it breaks the isolation they often feel from being confined to their homes.

"Your whole demeanor changes when you can get out of your house and just go around the block and around city streets," Julie said. "It's helped my social life a whole bunch. I can get out and ride, see my neighbors, and say hi." 👓

CHAPTER 9

Features to Look for When Buying an E-Bike

"Nothing compares to the simple pleasure of a bike ride."
– *Former U.S. President John F. Kennedy*

"To bike or not to bike: that is not a question."
– *Unknown*

Now it's time to dive more deeply into the technical details of what to look for when shopping for an e-bike or e-trike. This information will help you select the bike that offers the best quality for your needs and your budget. After reading this chapter, you will be better equipped for your next visit to a bike store, or if you prefer, for shopping online for your next e-bike.

Does it really matter which components and features your new e-bike has? Yes and no. As noted in previous chapters, owners of e-bikes tend to be very happy with their purchases, regardless of which bike they ride. So on the surface, differences in key components may not seem to matter.

On the other hand, those most knowledgeable about e-bikes and who have ridden multiple models will tell you that certain features are indeed worth paying extra to get. With the right components, you can expect a smoother ride, improved safety, greater longevity for your e-bike, and overall better performance.

This chapter won't make you an expert, but it will equip you with the fundamentals you need to know to make a wiser choice when shopping for an e-bike.

Understanding E-Bike Batteries

The most expensive component on your e-bike is also one of the most important: the battery. After all, an electric bike is useless without a battery. Steer clear of anything other than lithium batteries, especially if shopping for a used e-bike. Not much more than a decade ago, some e-bikes still came with lead-acid batteries, similar to the batteries used in cars. They were heavier and far less efficient than today's lithium batteries. Don't buy an e-bike, new or used, with anything other than a lithium battery.

Here are some of the common e-bike battery specifications you will need to know:

Volts: Most batteries in the e-bike market are lithium batteries with 36 or 48 volts. Choosing a bike with the larger 48-volt battery will give you the most "horsepower" from your e-bike battery, resulting in longer range and greater efficiency. On the other hand, if you ride on relatively flat terrain and don't expect to ride more than 20 to 25 miles per day, an e-bike with a 36-volt battery can serve you just as well and will cost less to purchase.

Amps: This is a measure of the capacity of your battery for transporting energy.

Amp hours (Ah): A key factor in battery performance is the range per charge, measured in amp hours or Ah. A standard e-bike battery may be rated for around 10 Ah, capable of propelling an average-weight person on a flat road for up to 20 miles on a single charge. Higher-priced e-bikes may offer batteries with an extended range, such as 12 to 17 Ah.

The amp hour rating has a direct impact on how far you can travel per charge on your e-bike. If you are of average or less weight, ride on flat roads, and have no real desire to travel more than 20 or so miles per day on your e-bike, then a lower-capacity 10 Ah battery is sufficient. Otherwise, it pays to buy an extended-range battery, which in many cases will allow you to travel 40, 50 or more miles on a single charge. A higher Ah rating is also better for heavier riders or for riding on hilly roads.

Many e-bikes offer a choice of batteries at the time of purchase. If so, opting for the extended-range (higher Ah) battery is an option worth choosing, especially if you plan to go on longer rides or ride in hilly terrain.

Watts: Simply multiply volts x amps to get watts.

Watts hours (Wh): Another commonly quoted measurement is watt hours, or Wh. This is an estimate of the total number of watts that can be run through the battery per hour. It's calculated by multiplying the battery's voltage by its amps hour rating. A larger number of Wh is preferable for getting maximum time and distance per charge. For instance, a 36-volt, 11.6 Ah battery would have a Watts hour rating of 417.6. A 48-volt, 11.6 Ah battery would have a longer Watts hour rating of 556.8 Wh. A bike battery with a higher Wh rating will travel for a longer distance per battery charge, which could be important if you plan to do longer rides.

Battery Location

Different brands and models of e-bikes install the battery at different spots on the bike. **The most common locations are (1) along the downtube of the frame in front of the rider, (2) behind (below) the seat post mounted vertically, or (3) lying flat on the rear rack above the rear wheel.** There are respectable bike brands that follow each of these placement locations with few if any complaints from owners. All other factors being equal, the first two locations (along the frame's downtube or behind the seat post) are preferable because they do a better job of balancing the bike's weight. The battery is heavy, weighing several pounds, so where it is placed on the bike can make a difference in the bike's weight distribution and performance.

See Chapter 11 for tips on how to care for your e-bike battery.

Motors: Size and Types

Next to the battery, the most important component on any e-bike is the motor. It's what pushes the bike forward when you use pedal assist or the throttle. The good news is that compared with batteries, motors are relatively trouble-free. Most e-bike motors will perform well for many years with hardly a thought about them from the bike's owner.

The size (power rating) of the motor may be dictated by where you live. In the UK and the European Union, for instance, e-bikes with motors larger than 250 watts are put into a different classification and not allowed on bike paths. In the U.S., motors may be as large as 750 watts, although e-bikes with 350- and 500-watt motors are more common. In Canada, the maximum wattage is 500.

While you might think higher wattage means more power or speed, the reality is not so simple. Several variables come into play, including the location of the motor (see next paragraph), the controller, and the battery. All of these components work together to power your e-bike. A 350-watt motor in some cases may feel as powerful or more so than another bike with a 500-watt motor. As a general statement, a higher-wattage motor is going to give you the maximum power that you may need if you are a heavier rider or live in an area where climbing hills is a challenge. Otherwise, most any size motor on a properly configured modern e-bike will be sufficient for recreational cycling and running errands, especially for average-size riders on mostly flat terrain.

Mid-Drive vs. Hub-Mounted Motors

Where the motor is located on the bike can also impact performance, reliability, and owner satisfaction. Most e-bikes come with hub-mounted motors on one of the wheels. Two-wheel e-bikes typically have the motor on the rear wheel, while trikes can have the motor on either the front or rear wheel. E-bike conversion kits typically come with front-wheel hub motors.

In recent years, a different motor placement, the mid-drive, has gained in popularity. Mid-drives are becoming more common on many higher-end, premium brands and models. Mid-drive configurations mount the motor in the crank, between the pedals.

It's not a clear-cut choice between which motor placement is "better" for all e-bike riders. Let's compare the two choices:

Advantages of Mid-Drive Motors

Photo used by permission of Bosch.

Proponents of mid-drive motors say they ride more naturally, more like a regular bicycle, especially when linked as they usually are with a torque sensor (discussed below). Rear-hub drives on the back wheel, by contrast, tend to push the rider forward rather than fostering a more natural pedal feel.

Mid-drive motors may be more efficient at climbing hills and riding for longer distances.

Another advantage of mid-drive motors is the better weight balance they provide, since they are centrally located on the bike, under the rider, low toward the ground. By contrast, a hub motor can make the rear wheel feel heavy and create balance issues. A hub motor mounted on the front wheel, common on e-bike conversion kits, can make steering more difficult.

One final benefit of mid-drives is tire maintenance. If you have a flat on the rear wheel of a hub-drive e-bike, it won't be an easy job to change the tube because the motor is mounted on the rear wheel. On a mid-drive bike, removing the rear wheel on an e-bike is no harder than doing so on a regular bike.

Advantages of Hub-Mounted Motors

Hub-mounted motors are cheaper for the manufacturer, helping keep the overall cost of the bike lower.

Hub-mounted motors typically require no maintenance, run quietly, and last a long time with little fuss. Mid-drive motors, by contrast, are more complex and thus more likely to need maintenance.

If your chain breaks on an e-bike powered by a mid-drive motor, you are out of luck. You cannot proceed on your ride without the chain. By contrast, on a hub-mounted bike, if the chain breaks, you can still cruise home using the throttle since the motor pushes the rear wheel rather than driving the chain.

Chains will receive more wear-and-tear on a mid-drive motor due to the added strain, and may be more likely to break. You don't have this problem with hub-mounted motors.

So which type of motor should you buy? **Even if you have the money to purchase a more expensive e-bike with a mid-drive motor, I would suggest first test-riding bikes with both motor placements to see which you prefer.** Test them on straight paths and on hills. Don't shy away from buying a bike just because it has a hub-mounted drive. Because it's cheaper doesn't necessarily mean it's inferior. You can find happiness on two wheels regardless of where the motor is located on your e-bike.

For now, rear-wheel, hub-mounted motors remain the standard on most new e-bikes. They serve the needs of average recreational cyclists well. Because of their cost advantage and reliability, hub-mounted motors are likely to be around for many years.

Making Sense of Sensors

It is hard to discuss motor placement without also addressing the issue of cadence sensors versus torque sensors. Most, but not all, e-bikes with mid-drive motors also have **torque** sensors. Most e-bikes with hub-mounted motors come with the less-expensive **cadence** sensor.

Most e-bikes sold in the U.S. and Canada use what is called a cadence sensor on the pedal crank to engage the power on the bike, known as pedal assist, or PAS. Using a magnet on the pedal crank, a cadence sensor turns the electric motor power on when the rider pedals and turns it off when the rider stops pedaling. It's a simple, inexpensive system that works well but has its drawbacks. It functions as more of an on/off switch, rather than sensing how much power is needed at a given time.

You receive less exercise benefit on an e-bike with a cadence sensor because you don't have to exert as much effort when pedaling. Some cyclists complain that e-bikes with cadence sensors feel jerky and unnatural. In their favor, e-bikes with cadence sensors require less effort to pedal, making them preferable for many senior adults, and especially those with weaker leg muscle strength and those suffering from joint pain.

Torque sensors, by contrast, require more effort to pedal, which is both good and bad for senior e-bike riders. One advantage is that torque sensors provide better leg exercise, but at the same time they may test the physical limits of some riders. Torque sensors measure not just whether the rider is pedaling but how hard. The more effort the cyclist is putting into pedaling, the more power that will be supplied.

Advocates say torque sensors, usually paired with a mid-drive motor, provide a smoother ride that feels more like riding a regular bike, except with power assist. Because of the higher price of the components, torque sensors are usually found only on more premium-priced e-bikes.

One factor to be aware of is that most e-bikes equipped with mid-drive motors and torque converters do not have throttles. If having a throttle is important to you, then you will need to stick with the more common design using a hub-mounted motor and cadence sensor.

So what should you, the average e-bike consumer, do? Like with the question of hub drives versus mid-drives, there is no clear answer as to which sensor technology is "better." It depends on the rider and your budget. Torque sensors are favored by many avid cycling enthusiasts. If you want a mid-drive motor, it is likely to be paired with a torque sensor. Cadence sensors are typically coupled with a hub-mounted motor.

In the end, your budget may dictate which sensor your bike has. The majority of e-bikes, at least in North America, come with hub motors and cadence sensors.

The truth is that the type of sensor you have won't greatly affect your happiness as an e-bike owner. Millions of e-bike owners are happily riding their bikes, and it's likely that the majority of them have no idea whether their bike has a cadence or torque sensor, or even what a sensor is. Don't let anyone try to convince you that because your e-bike does not have a torque sensor (or a mid-drive motor) that it is somehow an inferior e-bike. You can enjoy years of great exercise, reliable riding, bike touring, and pure enjoyment regardless of which system your e-bike has.

Throttles: Do You Need One?

The most controversial component on e-bikes is the throttle. Some e-bike enthusiasts view throttles as indispensable, essential equipment. They wouldn't buy an e-bike without one. Others think throttles should be outlawed. In fact, many countries, including those in the European Union, ban throttles on "pedelecs," the name used for lower-powered e-bikes most comparable to Class 1 e-bikes in the United States. Other jurisdictions require licensing or age restrictions on the use of e-bikes with throttles.

Similar to the throttle on a motorcycle or moped, an e-bike throttle propels the bike forward with no need for the rider to pedal. It's like coasting downhill on a bike except that with a throttle you can "coast" indefinitely (as long as the battery still has its charge) and even "coast" up hills.

Throttles come in two types, either thumb-controlled or wrist-twist. The twist model, typically built into the right-side handlebar grip, works more like a motorcycle or scooter throttle. Twist throttles are preferred by some but have a couple of drawbacks. One is that the wrist-twisting motion over a full day of cycling can cause wrist pain for some riders. Second, twist throttles can be more easily accidentally engaged at the wrong time, leading to accidents. If shopping for an e-bike with a throttle, try models with both types of throttles and see what seems more comfortable to you. There are fans of both styles.

In contrast to a motorcycle, most e-bikes in the U.S. with throttles (Class 2) top out at 20 mph when using only the throttle. You may be able to pedal the bike faster than 20 mph, but that is as fast as it will go on throttle-only.

It is this ability to propel a bike forward without pedaling that makes throttles controversial. Critics of throttles argue that if an e-bike is equipped with a throttle and the rider no longer has to pedal, it is no longer a bicycle. Traditional cyclists, especially, can find it annoying to be passed on trails by an e-bike rider who isn't pedaling but using only the throttle. They sometimes accuse these throttle-only e-bike cyclists of being "cheaters."

Especially in the U.S. and Canada, throttles are popular with the majority of e-bike owners. Most new e-bikes sold in these markets come standard with throttles, although there are notable exceptions. One of these is Trek, a higher-end American bike manufacturer that does not include throttles on its line of popular e-bikes. According to its website, Trek believes throttles can be a safety hazard, causing cyclists to lose control. In Trek's defense, it is undeniably true that some e-bike accidents do happen when riders hit the throttle at the wrong time, causing the bike to surge. In my opinion, this is largely a risk for inexperienced riders who have not yet learned how to use the throttle properly and can be overcome with more practice.

Benefits of E-Bike Throttles

There are several arguments to be made in favor of throttles, especially when used in conjunction with pedal assist. Here are three:

Throttles can be a safety feature. While companies such as Trek make a valid argument that throttles can be unsafe on e-bikes in certain circumstances, it is also true that, when properly used, throttles can make cycling safer. Throttles can help e-bike riders avoid wobbles and falls when taking off, either initially or at intersections. Wobbly take-offs are a common problem for inexperienced riders, those with poor balance, and other cyclists who have trouble controlling an e-bike due to its extra weight and power. A gentle touch on the throttle is all that is needed to set an e-bike safely in motion.

Another example of how throttles can provide a safety benefit is when a rider uses the throttle to hurry across an intersection or quickly get out of the way of another vehicle. In this scenario, the throttle is like the accelerator in a car. Sometimes you need to push the accelerator hard to get across traffic quickly or avoid a collision. The same is true for throttles on e-bikes.

Throttles can be a helpful aid to senior adults and others who are not in top physical shape. Even if a senior cyclist pedals 75 to 95 percent of the time, having the option to take an occasional rest from pedaling by using the throttle can keep seniors riding farther and not tiring out so quickly.

Throttles open up cycling opportunities for people with disabilities and other health limitations. Throttles give riders with breathing issues, degenerative diseases, and other disabilities the assurance that they can enjoy their ride and not worry about being able to get home. For many of them, not having a throttle would mean the end of their cycling adventures and a poorer overall quality of life. Even if they only pedal less than one-third of the time, or none at all, they are better off being outdoors and in motion versus sitting at home in front of the TV. While able-bodied riders of all ages should want to pedal most of the time for optimal fitness benefits, let's not be too quick to judge other riders who may be doing the best they can, even if that means using the throttle most of the time. Remember, we may be in their shoes one day.

What You Need to Know About Brakes

One important way that most of today's e-bikes differ from the older bikes we rode in the past is their brakes. E-bikes are heavier and potentially travel faster than traditional bikes, so they need stronger, better brakes. For added safety, most e-bike brakes come with a kill switch that automatically turns off the motor whenever you apply the brakes, even slightly.

Most e-bikes today have disc brakes, similar to the brakes on our cars. Disc brakes use pads and rotors. You can spot an e-bike that has disc brakes by looking at its wheels. They will have a large, circular, usually silver plate called a rotor. Disc brakes come in two types, mechanical and hydraulic. Most lower-end and many average-priced e-bikes will come equipped with mechanical disc brakes. They work sufficiently well for the average cyclist, but hydraulic disc brakes are considered to have superior stopping power. Most of the more expensive e-bikes have hydraulic disc brakes.

An exciting new development for e-bikes is the recent introduction of anti-locking brake systems (ABS). Already common on cars, trucks, and motorcycles, ABS systems are being developed by bike component makers including Bosch. ABS brakes provide better control and stability when braking. They eliminate the common problem of front-wheel lock-up, when front brake pressure exceeds the rear brake's pressure. When front wheel lock-up occurs, bike riders are often thrown head-first over the bike's handlebars. A study by Bosch estimated that if all e-bikes had ABS brakes, up to 29 percent of all accidents could be avoided. At this time, only a relatively few higher-end e-bikes come equipped with ABS braking systems but hopefully they will someday become the industry standard, as they now are in the automotive business.

Chapter 11 will provide you with the information you need to know on how to care for your e-bike's brakes.

Choosing the Right Tires

Bike tires come in a range of sizes, including different diameter and width sizes. Which tire size is best for you depends on several factors, the most important being where and how you plan to ride your e-bike. Road bikes that are built lightweight for speed, sometimes referred to as racing bikes, use very thin tires with extra high air pressure in order to minimize friction with the ground and improve speed. They also produce a harsher ride. At the other extreme, so-called "Fat Bikes" use tires that are 3.0 to 5.0 inches wide, making them ideal for going off-road on dirt paths and in sand. If you've ever seen the bikes that are rented to tourists at the beach, those were probably fat-tire bikes. Wide tires provide a smooth, cushiony ride, but are harder to pedal if you are not using electric power.

Most e-bikes bought by seniors come in between these two extremes when it comes to tire width. Cruiser bikes, with their upright handlebars and comfortable seats, typically have tires in the 1.75 to 2.50 inch width range. This size tire offers a good compromise, allowing the bike to be easy to pedal and control yet still offer a cushioned, comfortable ride. Tires in this size range are ideal for your e-bike if you primarily plan to ride on paved or hard-packed trails or use your bike on neighborhood roads and city streets. Most likely this describes how and where you will ride your e-bike.

While most e-bikes designed for mature riders are going to offer the size tires described above, fat-tire bikes are growing in popularity with seniors. They provide the most comfortable ride. Even though these fatter, heavier tires would be difficult to pedal on a traditional bike, on an e-bike they are not a problem. Fat-tire bikes are especially popular on smaller bikes and folding bikes that are favored by RV owners and others who like to take their bikes with them on camping trips, to national parks, and even to beaches.

Electric trikes typically sport thinner tires than cruiser bikes, with 1.5-inch widths being common. Fat tires are growing in popularity on e-trikes as well, offering a smoother ride and better off-road performance.

Tires are also measured by their diameter, with the 26-inch tire regarded as the "standard" size tire for adult bicycles, both traditional and electric. Many adult bicycles also come in a smaller version with 24-inch tires, a good choice for shorter riders who still want a cruiser-style bike. Taller riders can choose bikes with tires as large as 29 inches.

On smaller e-bikes and folding models, the most common size is the 20 inch tire, although some have an even smaller 16 inch tire. If you are shopping for a small e-bike, go with models that have 20 inch tires, not the 16 inch, unless you are quite certain that your rides will be of short duration. Small e-bikes with 20 inch tires perform remarkably similar to larger bikes and can accommodate riders of nearly all heights.

Electric trikes typically have either 20 or 24 inch diameter tires.

Wondering what to do if you have a flat tire? Read Chapter 11 for suggestions and best practices.

Suspension Systems Take the Bounce Out of Your Ride

Many mid-range and higher-end electric bikes include some form of suspension to help absorb shocks from bumpy roads, potholes, railroad crossings, and other obstacles. Purchasing an e-bike with a good suspension system makes sense for most seniors, who want their rides to be as smooth as possible. At our ages, none of us wants a jarring, bouncy ride.

Suspension systems come in two main types, one of which can be easily added to almost any bike. The first is a **shock-absorbing suspension built into the front tire fork.** Ideally, look for bikes that come equipped with this suspension since it would be difficult to add later. The second method is a **seat post with built-in shock-absorbing suspension.** Some bikes come standard with a suspension seat post, but if your e-bike doesn't have it, you can buy after-market suspension seat posts and easily remove and replace the bike's original seat post.

Shopping for an E-Bike

The information in this chapter should prove valuable when you shop for an e-bike. You now know far more than the average e-bike buyer. While you don't need to be a cycling expert, it pays to have some knowledge prior to visiting a bike shop. You will better understand why the shop employees are recommending one bike over another. If you choose to shop online, this chapter will be especially helpful.

Since you won't have bike store employees to guide you, you need some rational criteria for choosing one online e-bike over another. Using this chapter, you can create a checklist of components to look for when buying your next e-bike and be able to make a wiser choice.

There is no one bike style or brand that is the "best" for all riders and circumstances. Getting the right bike for you will make for a more enjoyable experience. Once you catch the e-bike "bug" and start dreaming of new places to explore with your e-bike, you just might decide you need more than one e-bike to meet your varied riding needs! After all, if one e-bike brings you so much pleasure, just think what owning two or three of them could do for you!

IMPORTANT: **After buying your new e-bike, be sure to read** Chapter 10 **before riding it. You will learn key safety and riding tips to make your e-bike cycling experience safer and more fun. What you will learn in the next chapter will reduce your chances of spills and other accidents that can result in serious injury, or worse. It's an important chapter you don't want to miss.**

In the Rider Profile following this chapter, you will hear how a fitness-minded couple are using e-bikes for both exercise and to enhance their travel opportunities. 👓

Bob Jones and Debra Landre

Travel-Loving Fitness Couple
Stays Active With E-bikes

"The surgeons kept telling me that the best thing for me was cycling."

Bob Jones and Debra Landre have always been competitive athletes. He's on a softball team and has twice hiked the nearly 2,200-mile Appalachian Trail, from Maine to Georgia. She has competed at the state and national levels as a lead paddler on dragon boat racing teams. They enjoy kayaking together too.

Knee and shoulder injuries eventually caught up with Deb. After knee-replacement surgery, she realized she could no longer do the 6-, 8- and 10-mile hikes she used to do. Meanwhile, nagging shoulder injuries put an end to her dragon-boat career.

"The surgeons kept telling me that the best thing for me was cycling," Deb said.

"I hadn't cycled for awhile, so Bob said 'let's get e-bikes. Let's try them out and see if we like them.' It was the best decision we ever made."

Owning e-bikes has been life-changing for this very fitness-minded couple.

Bob, 67, and Deb, 65, now keep Trek Verve e-bikes at their homes in Central Florida and in France. Even when doing home exchanges in the UK and Europe, cycling is part of their routine. Deb said she especially enjoys riding on the UK's towpaths and canal roads.

Cycling plays a key role in nearly all of their travel planning. Whether traveling in their RV or on their boat, the bikes go with them. The couple typically travels 7,000 to 10,000 miles per year in their RV, and they now make it a point to research bike trails along the route and ride as many of them as possible. They've ridden some of the most popular bike trails in the U.S., including the Katy Trail in Missouri and the Great Allegheny Passage (GAP) Trail in Pennsylvania. They've ridden other trails in Arkansas, Virginia, New York, and other states.

Bob said one of the best trails so far was in Nova Scotia, Canada.

"It was heaven on earth. Just incredible."

Bob and Deb have another companion when they ride their e-bikes — their dog. He travels either in a trailer attached to one of their bikes or in a "mommy pack."

Bob and Deb are sold on the benefits of e-bike cycling for senior adults who want to remain active for as long as possible. ⚬➤

"*The recumbent seat is like sitting at the kitchen table seat; it's a regular seat and a lot more comfortable.*"

RODGER PRICE (PAGE 209)

CHAPTER 10

Keeping Safe While Riding Your E-Bike

" ... bicycling isn't just a matter of balance. It's a matter of faith. You can keep upright only by moving forward. You have to have your eyes on the goal, not the ground. I'm going to call that the Bicyclist's Philosophy of Life."

— *Best-selling author Susan Vreeland in "Clara and Mr. Tiffany"*

"As a kid I had a dream. I wanted to own my own bicycle. When I got the bike, I must have been the happiest boy in Liverpool, maybe the world. I lived for that bike. Most kids left their bike in the backyard at night. Not me. I insisted on taking mine indoors and the first night I even kept it in my bed."

— *John Lennon of The Beatles*

Even if you rode a bike regularly as a child or young adult, it's different this time.

Today's electric bikes are heavier, faster, and more complex than the bikes we rode decades ago. Like it or not, we've changed too. We're not kids anymore. Our reaction times are slower. Our sense of balance and coordination isn't as keen as it once was. We don't have the strength or stamina we had back then.

For all of these reasons, it's important to understand how to smoothly and safely ride an e-bike, no matter what your age. It's not hard. You don't need special strength or athleticism. Nearly anyone can ride an e-bike, but there are things you need to know to keep safe and avoid accidents. That's what you will learn in this chapter. Be sure to read it before you start riding your shiny new e-bike.

Don't Become an Accident Statistic

No matter what you do in life, there is always risk. A relative of mine stepped out of her house and into her garage, fell and broke her ankle, requiring surgery and months of rehab. Someone in my neighborhood tripped on her dog's leash while out for a walk, breaking a leg.

Riding a bicycle is not considered a high-risk activity, but by nature it is not without risk. After all, a cyclist is propelling him or herself forward while balancing atop a machine with two relatively thin tires and no surrounding cage for protection. Add to that the fact that bicyclists are riding on paths or roads often shared by cars, trucks, pedestrians and other cyclists, and you have a formula for potential trouble, especially if good cycling habits are not practiced. This is why it's important to devote a chapter to safety.

In 2019, the National Safety Council says 1,089 cyclists died in U.S. accidents, most involving accidents with motor vehicles. That's an increase of 37 percent over the past decade. Much of that increase is explained by the rising popularity of cycling. In addition, 417,485 cycling injuries were treated in U.S. emergency rooms in 2019, according to the Consumer Product Safety Commission.

Anecdotal evidence, if not hard statistics, confirms that **more seniors are having accidents as they return to cycling after many years of not riding.** E-bikes require more caution when riding due to their extra weight and faster speed, especially in the hands of inexperienced cyclists.

While this number of fatalities is alarming for those of us who love cycling, it has to be viewed in context. In the same year, 39,107 people died in motor vehicle accidents in the U.S., according to the National Safety Council. Another 4,572 people died from accidents at work.

The riskiest place to be? According to the NSC, it's in and around your home. In 2019, the NSC says 131,400 people died in accidents in and around their homes.

This discussion is not intended to alarm you or to discourage you from buying and enjoying any type of bicycle — traditional, e-bike or e-trike. Rather, it is to remind you of the risks and encourage you to adopt safe cycling habits, as outlined in this chapter.

Cycling's Benefits Outweigh the Risks

Millions of seniors around the world are regularly cycling, and an increasing number of them are riding e-bikes and e-trikes. They feel much better as a result and are having the time of their lives. Plenty of senior adults in their 70s, 80s, and even 90s are still riding e-bikes successfully. Their physical and mental health are better thanks to their cycling habit. They won't (and in most cases shouldn't) stop cycling until they can absolutely not do so any longer. If you're reading this book, odds are good that you aren't too old to ride an e-bike!

Whether you drive (or ride in) a car, take your boat out on the lake, play pickleball, or ride a bicycle, accidents can happen. The solution isn't to avoid all activities that involve risk but to find ways to minimize it. After all, what's the alternative? Stay home with your blinds closed and never venture out? What kind of life is that?

The Baby Boomer generation, for sure, isn't going to stay home with the blinds closed. No way. We're the most active generation of seniors yet. We are on the go and play hard. We're determined to wear out, not rust out. We want to remain active for as long as possible. We are going to do everything within our power to avoid the rocking chair and the nursing home.

So, don't give up on your dream of riding an e-bike simply because you've heard about people having accidents with them. You'll be missing out not only on better health but also a lot of fun!

With the safety and riding tips you will learn in this chapter, you too can join the growing ranks of Baby Boomers who are happily addicted to their e-bikes and riding them safely. Applying the suggestions made in this chapter can reduce your chances of becoming an accident statistic.

If you read only one chapter in this book (I hope you'll read all of them), then this is the one you most need to read. You will need this information regardless of which e-bike brand and model you buy. Even if you're an experienced cyclist but new to e-bikes, you will benefit from reading this chapter. It will equip you with the knowledge to become a safer rider and reduce your chances for accidents and injuries.

Let's first look at safety and riding tips unique to e-bikes.

Tips for Riding an E-bike Safely and Successfully

Fundamentally, an e-bike is still a bicycle. If you can ride a regular bike, you can ride an e-bike. At the same time, riding an e-bike successfully does involve some new skills and challenges not found on regular bikes.

The most obvious reason for this difference is that e-bikes have a source of power other than your legs. As with any powered vehicle, that extra power must be managed carefully to avoid negative consequences. Beyond that, the extra weight of an e-bike can make it perform differently in some circumstances and be harder to control.

Here are tips to help make your experience with e-bikes safer and more comfortable.

Consider Safety When Buying Your E-Bike: As discussed in Chapters 6 and 7, there are many styles of e-bikes and e-trikes to choose from. If you do not feel stable or safe on a larger (full size) e-bike, consider buying a smaller model such as a 24-inch or 20-inch e-bike. You may find that this smaller size feels more manageable, especially if you are a shorter or lighter-weight person.

The frame design can also impact safety. Many seniors choose step-through frame designs without a high top bar. This makes the bike easier, and safer, to mount and dismount. A surprising number of accidents happen as riders are mounting and dismounting their bikes.

If balance and coordination are your concerns, then consider buying an e-trike, with three wheels. Trikes are more stable and you no longer have to worry about wobbly starts and falling off. You can flip a trike, but if you ride sensibly and cautiously, flipping a trike is not nearly as likely as falling off a two-wheel bike. Plus, if you do fall off a trike, you are much closer to the ground.

Because buying the right bike in the first place is so critical to a safe and successful e-bike experience, it makes sense for most consumers to purchase their e-bike from a local bike shop where they can ask questions and test ride various models. This is especially true for first-time e-bike buyers.

Get Acquainted Slowly with Your New E-Bike: When first introduced to e-bikes, many seniors are excited and can't wait to take one for a ride. Other seniors are a bit scared or concerned about their capabilities to handle an e-bike at their age. After being accustomed to riding a traditional bicycle, and maybe after not having ridden ANY bike for many years, starting to ride an e-bike for the first time can be intimidating. As soon as you start pedaling, the power kicks in. And the power is real. On your first ride, you may feel like you've straddled a motorcycle or a rocket rather than a bicycle.

Trust me, this is a learning curve you can master — and quickly. Don't let this initial reaction scare you away from the joys and benefits of riding an e-bike. You will love it once you get the hang of it. Hey, you're a Baby Boomer. You can do this!

The best advice is to get acquainted slowly with your new e-bike. Take it one step at a time. Get to know how it feels and how well balanced it is.

Here are some suggestions for your introduction to your new e-bike:

- **Get Proper Fit:** When you mount the bike for the first time, make sure it is properly fitted for you, with the handlebars and seat in a comfortable position. If you bought your e-bike from a bike store, the staff should help you with these adjustments before leaving the store.

- **Put Helmet on First:** Strap on your bike helmet BEFORE straddling the bike or turning on its power (read more about helmets later in this chapter).

- **Know Your Bike:** Have someone at the bike shop, or a friend who is experienced with e-bikes, explain all of the controls on the handlebars so you understand how the bike works. You need to know how to use the brakes, gears, and pedal assist before starting to ride.

- **Start With Power Off:** Next, try riding your new e-bike for the first time in a safe area with no traffic, and do so with all of the power turned OFF. That's right, just ride it like a regular bicycle.

Don't use the pedal assist or throttle but do make sure the bike is in the lowest gear to make pedaling easier. Even if this is a bit difficult for you, it will help you get the feel for the bike. Ride it around the parking lot or down to the corner and back. Do this as many times as necessary to get comfortable with your new bike and how it works.

⚙ **Introduce Pedal Assist Slowly:** After this first trial run without using any power, you are now ready to turn on the e-bike's pedal assist and try the first (lowest) PAS level, making sure you are pointing straight ahead, with your hands on the handlebar grips, and ready to step up your speed. Now gently pedal. Depending on the type of e-bike you purchased, you will likely feel the surge of the pedal assist immediately.

If you've followed these steps, a big smile is going to come across your face about now. **You are going to like the way the power assist feels!** Don't worry yet about the higher levels of pedal assist, just stay in PAS 1 or 2 initially. If necessary, use your gears at this point, but don't go into a higher PAS yet. You'll have plenty of power for most low-speed applications. Practice enough in a safe area so you feel totally comfortable on your new bike. Do this as many times as necessary before venturing for the first time onto city streets or bike trails.

Make the Throttle Your Best Friend: If your new e-bike has a throttle, it can help make your riding safer when used properly. One smart use of a throttle is to help you get off to a smoother start. Many seniors complain about wobbly starts and even falling off the bike when trying to start from a dead stop. The heavier weight of an e-bike contributes to this problem, along with reduced balance and coordination as we age. A light touch on the throttle when you are ready to move forward will give you the momentum you need to make a smooth, successful start. This is one of the most common ways that experienced e-bike users use their throttles. Like any new technique, it may feel awkward at first, but keep trying it. With a throttle, wobbly starts will be a thing of the past.

In similar fashion, a light touch on the throttle can help you get back in motion after being stopped at an intersection, stop sign, or red light. Just make sure you have your front wheel pointing straight ahead and you are settled on the bike before pushing the throttle. Once you push it, the bike is going to jump forward.

Throttles are also useful for delivering that important extra boost going up a hill, passing someone, or just to give yourself an occasional rest from pedaling. What you don't want to do is become dependent on the throttle so that you use it instead of pedaling. To get the exercise benefits an e-bike is capable of providing, you need to pedal as much as possible.

Don't let the throttle become a crutch that keeps you from exercising. Push yourself if necessary, but pedal. It's fine to use your throttle to take an occasional rest from pedaling, but if you aren't interested in pedaling, then maybe a scooter or moped is a better fit for you. As noted previously in this book, some riders have health limitations that require them to use the throttle most of the time or even exclusively, so don't give fellow cyclists a hard time if they are using the throttle a lot. You never know their circumstances.

Do you feel that you are too weak to pedal most of the time, even if you don't have a disability that prohibits you from pedaling? That's OK, especially if you haven't exercised regularly in recent years. Here's my suggestion: Do the best you can at first, but enjoy the ride and get comfortable with the bike. Use the throttle as much as necessary. Make cycling with your new e-bike a habit, cycling as many days per week as possible. Each day or week, try to pedal more and use the throttle less. If you only pedal 20 percent of the time during Week 1, push yourself a bit and up it to 25 percent in Week 2.

Before you know it, you will be pedaling the majority of the time and feel much better about yourself. As a bonus, you are going to feel your health improving, with more energy and stronger leg muscles.

Start and Stop in PAS 0. Another good safety practice is to **keep the pedal assist turned off or in PAS 0 (depending on how your bike is configured) until you mount the bike and are ready to ride.** This helps to avoid jerky, too-fast starts. On many e-bikes, especially those with cadence sensors (See Chapter 9 for a fuller discussion of sensors), even PAS 1 gives the bike a surprisingly strong push forward. If you are not settled on your bike or have to make a quick turn into the street after exiting your driveway, this sudden thrust can cause you to lose control. I personally like to start pedaling without PAS power and not turn it on until I am out of my driveway and riding straight in the street. As you build leg muscle from regular cycling, you may even find you can ride a block, then two blocks, and then maybe a mile or more before turning the pedal assist from PAS 0 to a higher number. You will be riding your e-bike like a regular bicycle, using only your leg muscles. Even then, it's comforting to have the throttle available when needed for an extra boost. For similar safety reasons, I also turn the pedal assist off (or PAS 0) at the end of the ride, before re-entering my driveway.

Beware of Accidental PAS Surges When Stopped: When riding our bikes, many of us stop to chat with a friend or neighbor along the way, or just stop at an intersection while waiting for cars to pass. The best (safest) practice in such situations is to take both feet off the pedals and stand squarely on the ground when stopped. Otherwise, if one or both of your legs are on the pedals while stopped and you accidentally lean on the pedals or move them, the PAS will kick in and surge you forward. This may cause you to lose control of the bike or fall off. Do not move the pedals while you are stopped when using pedal assist. A safety feature that is standard on most new e-bikes is that when you squeeze either the right or left brake lever, it disengages the pedal assist. It's a good habit to keep one hand engaging a brake level whenever you are stopped. This will eliminate the risk of an accidental surge while stopped.

Turn Your E-Bike Off Before Dismounting: Many of us with e-bikes equipped with throttles have had the unpleasant experience of accidentally touching the throttle when we're not riding. In my case, I had finished my ride and was walking my new e-bike toward the shed to put it away for the evening. I mistakenly pushed down on the throttle. My e-bike surged ahead powerfully, even as I struggled to hold it back, unaware at first of what was happening. In a split second, my bike was out of control, like a wild horse, almost crashing into my nearby car. I got a couple of bruises, but thankfully nothing more serious. Needless to say, most of us only make that mistake once! Fortunately, it's one you can easily avoid. All you have to do is turn the bike's power off (not just the pedal assist but all power) when you finish your ride, before dismounting your bike. Then you can easily put your bike away without incident. Learn from my mistake and you will avoid this trauma!

Safe-Riding Rules Regardless of What Type of Bike You Ride

Now that we've discussed safe-riding techniques for e-bikes, let's look at more safety issues that apply to all cyclists, regardless of whether you ride a regular bike, an e-bike, or a trike. Read these carefully and be sure to practice safe cycling.

The Number One Safety Rule for All Cyclists: **Whether you're 7 or 70, the absolute best step you can take toward safer cycling is to wear a helmet.** About two-thirds of all cycling deaths, and one-third of all cycling accidents, involve the head and face, according to a report from Cleveland Clinic. Wearing a helmet can reduce the risk of head injury by up to 85 percent.

The author and family on a bike ride. If we can wear helmets in the Florida heat, anyone can – and should!

I cringe when I see people with no helmet bicycling on trails and city streets. They make the usual excuses. "I am only riding around the neighborhood," or "I'm not going that fast" or "It's too hot." One of the lamest excuses is "I'm not wearing a helmet because it will mess up my hair." Really? How about messing up your HEAD? That should be your greater concern. Even a low-speed crash can cause significant injuries. Even if your friends and family say you have a hard head, the truth is that skulls are no match for pavement or concrete. Always, always wear a helmet when riding a bike, even for short distances.

Interestingly, helmet usage varies by country. Helmet usage is lower in most of Europe than in the U.S. and Canada. Usage in the UK falls somewhere in between. Some of the lowest rates of adult helmet usage are in the Netherlands and Denmark, two nations where most adults ride bikes. Only 1 percent of adult cyclists in Amsterdam wear helmets. While the larger explanation is simply that cultural norms differ, a contributing factor is that because these countries have such well-developed bike infrastructure (lanes and paths), cyclists feel much safer riding there than in North America and therefore feel less compelled to don a helmet.

There is a push to promote more widespread helmet usage in parts of Europe. A recent study by DEKRA, a German company that does automotive testing and crash research, concluded that wearing a helmet when cycling reduces head injuries. It recommended that all cyclists wear helmets at all times.

Even many cyclists who wear helmets don't do so properly. Make sure the fit is snug so the helmet won't move around on your head. Wear the helmet level, not tilted back, so the forehead is always covered. Cleveland Clinic recommends that the bottom edge of the helmet should be one to two finger widths above the eyebrow.

Borrowing from a similar phrase many of us have used with children or grandchildren in our cars to encourage them to wear seatbelts, it is a good practice in cycling to say that "the bike won't move until the helmet is on."

In this book, I'm not going to wade into the discussion of which helmet to buy. Some experienced cyclists are very choosy about types and brands of helmets. After all, it's your head's safety we're talking about here. Talk to your more knowledgeable cycling friends and with bike shops about helmets. As with most products, not all helmets are created equal and you tend to get what you pay for. Thankfully, all helmets sold in the U.S. must meet minimum construction and safety standards set by the Consumer Products Safety Commission. Even so, higher-priced helmets may offer better protection, including helmets featuring newer safety technology such as MIPS or WaveCel.

The most important point is to buy and wear a helmet designed for bicycling, not which helmet brand or model you buy.

The Importance of a Proper Bike Fit

For safety, you need a bike that fits you properly. A bike that is too large or too heavy for you will be hard to steer and maneuver, especially when you need to take quick corrective action to avoid a crash. Many seniors find that full-size e-bikes with 26 inch tires are too large and harder to handle. This is especially true for shorter and lighter-weight riders, including many women, and for those in the higher age categories who may not have the muscle strength they once had. Adding to the problem, e-bikes are much heavier than regular bicycles, with most e-bikes weighing between 50 and 70 pounds. This can make them harder to manage, especially for some senior adults.

The solution for many of these seniors is to choose a smaller e-bike, either a 24-inch or 20-inch model. While they may not be that much lighter, the smaller size and lower sitting position makes them a better fit for some seniors. Small bikes with 20-inch tires, including many models that fold, are one of the fastest-growing segments of the e-bike market. With adjustable seats and handlebars, these smaller bikes can also be enjoyed by taller riders.

Whichever bike you buy, make sure it is fitted to you properly, including the handlebars, seat, and pedals. The local bike shop where you purchased the bike will help you make these adjustments. If you buy online, you may be able to pay a local bike shop to help fit you properly. At the least, ask a more experienced cycling friend for help.

Always Obey Traffic Laws

As cyclists, we can be inconsistent at times when it comes to obeying traffic laws. We want the right to use the road network alongside cars and trucks, but at the same time we don't always like to stop at stop signs or ride on the correct side of the street. Many cycling mishaps can be avoided simply by following traffic laws, which apply equally to motorists and cyclists. This includes stopping (full stops) at stop signs and traffic lights. It includes riding on the correct side of the road, flowing with the traffic. It includes signaling your intent when turning. If your bike isn't equipped with turn signals, and most are not, then it's important to use proper hand signals so motorists know when you plan to turn.

One risky behavior I see often on bike trails is when bicyclists ignore stop signs on cross roads, often not even slowing down. True, most of these cross roads are low-traffic and motorists will sometimes yield to cyclists anyway, but it's a dangerous assumption to make that either no vehicles will be on the cross road or that if there are they will stop for you. It's like playing Russian roulette. If you're sailing through an intersection on a bike at 12-to-20 mph and a motorist doesn't yield to you, you are going to crash and likely suffer serious injuries. It will be your fault, not the motorist's.

This flaunting of traffic laws seems to be part of the macho cycling culture, at least here in North America. Some cyclists seem to think they own the roads and can do what they want. For safety's sake and for the future of cycling as a serious choice for transportation, this culture needs to change. Make it a point to stop at cross roads that have stop signs and slow for yield signs, regardless of what other cyclists do. Observe speed limits on multi-purpose trails. Slow down around pedestrians and slower cyclists.

Make Sure Motorists Can See You

It's your job to make sure motorists can see you. Experienced cyclists often advise newcomers to always assume they are invisible to motorists when riding their bikes. **Do everything you can to make yourself visible, whether cycling during the day or after dark. It's always a good practice to wear brightly colored clothing or a safety vest.** I often wear a yellow vest like those people wear when directing traffic on the highway. It's a good idea to buy some brightly colored

(yellow, lime green, orange, etc.) shirts to wear when cycling. You can also buy reflective tape to attach to your shirts, jackets, helmet, or backpacks.

If you regularly ride in traffic in close proximity to motorized vehicles, you may want to go a step further and buy brightly colored shoes and/or reflective bands for your arms and legs. Adding reflective tape to your helmet can also improve your visibility. For better visibility at night, you can even add reflectors or lights to your bike's wheels.

Like helmets, it's interesting to note that the wearing of brightly-colored clothes and vests when cycling is much more common in the U.S. than in Europe. Why? The answer is simple. Cycling in much of Europe is much safer due to better networks of bike lanes and trails and the greater awareness motorists show toward cyclists there. Hopefully that will someday be true in the U.S. as well. In the meantime, it's up to you, the cyclist, to protect yourself and make sure you are seen by motorists.

Light Up Your Bike

Good lights should be standard equipment on all bikes, but unfortunately they are not. Even for bikes that come with lights, they are often too dim to provide good visibility. The purpose is not only to provide you with visibility to see the road if cycling after dark, but equally important to make you highly visible to motorists.

You need good-quality LED lights that run off your e-bike's battery or have their own lithium battery and are USB rechargeable. Avoid bike lights that use AA or AAA household batteries, but if this is all you have, buy the strongest, longest-lasting batteries possible and replace them at least annually. For rear lights, it's best to have a bright red light that can be set to flashing so motorists will see you.

Many experts say it's a good practice to use your headlight and taillight even when cycling during the day. Some cyclists use pulsating lights for daytime riding, with a white light in the front and red in the back. The purpose is to make sure motorists are aware of your presence. In my opinion, whether you need daytime lights depends on where you're riding. If you're riding on city streets or highways shared by motorists, then absolutely, use your lights, day and night. On the other hand, if you are riding inside a 55+ community or other low-traffic neighborhood or riding on a well-marked bike trail, you may not need lights during the day. Use your best judgment but always err on the side of safety.

An emerging trend on some new e-bikes is the inclusion of a brake light and, in some cases, turn signals. This is a promising trend that hopefully will become an industry standard within the next few years. This will help cars, other cyclists, and pedestrians who are behind you to know your intentions.

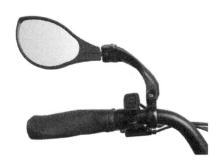

Install and Use A Rear-View Mirror

Another item that (in my opinion) should be standard equipment on bikes is a rear-view mirror. In order to ride safely, you have to be aware of your surroundings, including what's behind you. One of the more dangerous situations I often observe while riding on bike trails is cyclists with no mirrors and no idea when other cyclists are approaching them from behind. Very few e-bikes come with mirrors, so you will need to buy and install one before riding. In countries like the U.S. where cyclists and motorists drive on the right side of the road, mirrors should be mounted on the left side of the handlebars, although some cyclists prefer to have mirrors on both sides, which is fine.

It's not enough just to have a rear-view mirror. For it to keep you and other cyclists safe, you must stay vigilant at all times and use the mirror, just as you would in an automobile or truck. It may take time to get in the habit, but make it a point to watch your mirror regularly and always be aware of your surroundings.

A new trend is the use of rear-view cameras on bikes, with the viewing screen mounted on the handlebars. It can provide a wider, better view of what's behind you versus a mirror. One issue with such cameras, however, is scarce space on the handlebars for yet another screen, alongside the bike's controller display and a cellphone mount.

Watch for Tricky Road Surfaces

On a slippery road surface, it only takes a split second to lose control and have your bike slide out from under you. Because a bicycle only has two tires and they are relatively thin, it is much easier for a bicycle to lose control on a slick or slippery surface than a larger vehicle such as an automobile. Wet roads can be a problem for bikes, just like they are for motorists. Even more problematic for cyclists are loose items on the road that at first glance may not seem so dangerous. These include sand, pine needles, and leaves. Your best defense is to slow down and navigate turns with care.

Potholes can be a nightmare for cyclists. While hitting a modest pothole may be annoying while driving a car, doing the same while riding a bike is going to be much more jarring. Be especially watchful for potholes on wet streets and trails, as it is often hard to know if they are shallow or deep.

You must be vigilant 100 percent of the time while cycling, always on the watch for road signs, obstacles ahead, intersections, motorists, stray animals, other cyclists, and pedestrians. Remember all of those warnings about not texting while driving? Don't text while riding a bike either. If you must respond to a text message or take care of other urgent business on your cellphone, just pull off the road or trail (safely), take care of your business, and then resume your ride. It's much easier to pull over on a bike than when in a car.

Signage to keep you safe. Available as a free PDF from RoadTrafficSigns.com

Slow Down and Enjoy the Ride

A troubling trend within a segment of the e-bike public is the desire of some consumers to want to buy e-bikes that exceed the speed regulations. In the U.S., many e-bike owners purchase Class 3 e-bikes because they will go up to 28 mph using only the throttle. *If you've ever traveled on a bike at any speed over 20 mph, you understand that this is a very fast speed. A crash at those speeds can have catastrophic results for the cyclist.*

This craving for higher and higher speeds also explains why some trail networks and parks are banning Class 3 e-bikes – at those speeds, e-bikes become not just a nuisance, but a danger to other cyclists and pedestrians.

Even the Class 3 speed isn't fast enough for some e-bike owners. A common discussion on online e-bike forums is about how to tinker with your e-bike to make it go even faster. I've seen riders brag about how their e-bike will go 35 mph. That's insanely fast on a bicycle for anyone other than a trained and fit competitive racer.

In my opinion, and especially speaking primarily to an audience of senior-adult cyclists, **riding in excess of 20 mph on an e-bike is asking for trouble.** You are only one pothole away from a hospital visit. You are only one car pulling out of a driveway ahead of you or someone unexpectedly opening a car door away from serious injury. For these reasons, I do not recommend Class 3 e-bikes for senior riders. Why tempt yourself by buying a bike that will go this fast? Why buy a bike you can't even legally ride on many trails? And by all means, don't waste your time (and risk your life) by modifying your e-bike to go even faster.

Class 1 and Class 2 e-bikes sold in the U.S. are limited to 20 mph using only pedal assist or throttle. In the UK and European Union, the top speed for a pedelec is 15.5 mph. Those speeds (15.5 to 20 mph) are plenty fast for most bike riders, especially us aging Baby Boomers.

Besides, what's the rush? Excluding racing bikes in events like the Tour de France, bicycle riding for most of us is intended to be a leisurely, enjoyable activity. One wonderful benefit of riding a bike as opposed to faster forms of transportation like motorcycles and automobiles is that you get to see the world close up and appreciate its beauty. You can smell the flowers and wave at neighbors riding a bike leisurely at 10 to 15 mph, but you can't do that as well when you are riding at twice that speed.

Frank Cauthorn, a renowned long-distance bike tourer and sportsman, says it best in this quote:

"I love riding my bike and discovering and seeing things that people speeding by at 65 mph never notice. The slower pace of bicycle touring has a calming 'peaceful easy feeling.' I love riding my bicycle to the world's natural wonders and experiencing the beauty of mountains, lakes, rivers, hot springs, beaches."

For seniors in particular, one easy way to make e-bike riding safer is simply to slow down. Speed kills. For every additional 5 mph that you are cycling, the risk of injury from an accident increases significantly. A 15-mph crash will do considerably more harm than a 10-mph crash. When crashing a bike at speeds of 20 mph and higher, all bets are off.

Does your e-bike seem too fast? Talk with your dealer or manufacturer. Many e-bikes allow you to lower the top-end speed with a simple adjustment in the settings on the controller.

Avoid Night Riding

There is a strong correlation between bike fatalities and darkness. According to the U.S. National Highway Traffic Safety Administration, **most bike fatalities occur between 6 and 9 p.m, with the 9 p.m.-to-midnight time period also ranking high.** It's hard enough for motorists to see bikes during the day, let alone at night. It's harder for cyclists to see potholes and other road hazards at night. There's also a greater chance that motorists you are sharing the road with are going to be driving under the influence of alcohol or drugs in the evening and night hours. Even if they aren't intoxicated, drivers at these late hours are more likely to be tired and sleepy.

When you hear about late-night bike fatalities, unfortunately it is often an accident that could have been prevented by practicing safe-cycling rules. I recently observed a cyclist riding along a city street after dark, wearing dark clothing, no reflective vests or stickers, and only a minimal, inadequate headlight. He was riding on the wrong side of the street, facing traffic. What's worse, he was pulling a child carrier behind his bike. Sure enough, a car came toward him at a high rate of speed and almost hit him. The cyclist yelled at the driver, but in reality, it was largely his own fault.

Your best bet is to avoid night riding. As senior adults, riding after dark shouldn't be necessary for most of us. If you must ride after dark, then make sure you and your bike are up to the task. Wear bright, reflective clothing. Consider using reflective Velcro straps on your arms and ankles. Use as many lights as possible, front and back, and make sure they are bright. This may include flashing red lights on either the back of your bike or on your helmet or both.

Day or night, it's your job as a cyclist to make sure motorists can see you.

Cycling, Drinking, and Drugs Don't Mix

Watching out for intoxicated or stoned motorists is a bad enough problem for cyclists. Taking a ride on your bike when YOU are the one who is under the influence of alcohol or drugs is even worse. Riding a bike requires your full concentration, coordination, and attention.

Including substance-impaired motorists, 37 percent of all bike fatalities are alcohol-related. Never, ever ride under the influence.

It's hard to imagine why anyone would be so careless as to ride a bicycle under the influence of alcohol or drugs, but statistics show it's a significant contributing factor in many deadly bike accidents. The NHTSA says **26 percent of cyclists in fatal**

crashes in the U.S. had high levels of alcohol in their blood. If you add impaired motorists, 37 percent of all bike fatalities are alcohol-related. Thats's more than one-third of all cycling-related fatalities!

As noted above, evening hours are the most dangerous for cyclists and it's no coincidence that these are the same hours when alcohol and recreational drug use is the highest. Remove these two risk factors and you've greatly reduced your chances of being in a serious or fatal biking accident.

Riding a bike while under the influence is suicidal. Don't do it. Ever. If staying sober is a problem for you, get help. Until then, give your e-bike's keys to a trusted spouse or friend during hours of the day when you are prone to become intoxicated or high, so they can deny you the right to ride when you aren't capable.

Keep Your Ears Free to Hear Surrounding Noises

It's fun to listen to music, podcasts, audiobooks, or news shows while exercising. That's a habit that's been ingrained in us at least since the first battery-powered portable radios became popular. Remember the Sony Walkman and later the Apple iPod? Portable devices like these were wildly popular with walkers, runners, and cyclists. Today we have all sorts of convenient wired and wireless earplugs and earbuds to stream music or other programming from our cellphones or smart watches while we exercise.

Trouble is, safe cycling requires being able to hear sounds around us, from motorists to other cyclists shouting "On the left" or other helpful information to us. Keen listening skills and attention are important to safe cycling. You must always be aware of what is around you.

For this reason, **many trails prohibit the use of headphones, earplugs, and earbud devices while cycling. Most cycling groups**

strongly discourage the use of such audio devices. Unfortunately, plenty of riders ignore this advice and do it anyway.

The good news is that thanks to modern technology, there are safer ways to listen to your music or other programming while cycling. If you insist on using a headphone or earbuds, buy one of the newer models that allows you to switch to ambient sound mode. In this mode, you can still hear other noises around you while listening to your programming. You must remember to turn on this feature each time you ride in order to benefit from it.

An even better choice is a headphone that transmits audio through your bones, not through your ears. This may sound odd, but it works well. Bone-conduction headphones sit right in front of your ears, keeping your ears free to hear other sounds such as traffic and other cyclists. There are many brands of bone-conduction headsets available these days. This category has become popular with joggers and walkers as well as cyclists.

Yet another approach to listening to music and other programming while still being able to hear ambient noises is to go with a specially designed helmet that has speakers built in. The most popular brand of these "smart" helmets is Sena. Coupled with a cellphone or smartwatch, Sena helmets not only allow you to listen to your music or podcast but also to accept phone calls and hear GPS directions.

Your best choice is to avoid all audio distractions while cycling and enjoy the sounds of nature around you. If you do feel a need to listen to music or other programming, be sure to use one of these newer technologies to make your experience as safe as possible.

Dealing With Angry Dogs

"The police came and knocked on my door and told me my dog was chasing people on bikes. I told them that was ridiculous cause my dog doesn't even own a bike." - *Unknown*

That's a funny cycling joke, but in reality when you are riding your bike angry dogs can be a real problem.

I'm not sure what it is about dogs, but some of them sure love to chase people on bicycles! Most of the time, it's just the sport of the chase that motivates them. They aren't out for blood but have a jolly good time chasing us. Sometimes, however, a truly angry and potentially dangerous dog can tenaciously pursue you like a heat-seeking missile honed in on its target. That's a scary scenario when on a bicycle; you have little protection and nowhere to hide.

What is the best approach to deal with dogs while cycling? The answer is that it depends on you, the dog, and the situation.

Get a move on: If it's a smaller (or overweight) dog and you are on an open flat road with little traffic, your best bet may simply be to put your e-bike in high gear and a high PAS level (or full throttle) and outrun the dog. While many dogs can run fast, most can't do so for very long. They will quickly tire and give up the chase. Some larger or more athletically built dogs, on the other hand, will have the strength and the determination to overtake you.

Dismount with the bike between you and the dog: Based on the assumption that nine out of ten dogs that chase you are someone's pets and aren't really that aggressive, some cyclists choose to simply stop and get off their bike, keeping the bike between them and the dog. Or you can walk with the bike after dismounting.

Speak calmly: If the dog is within close range, try talking calmly to it, showing you are not a threat. Once you've ended the chase, many dogs will immediately lose interest. They may continue barking for a few minutes but will usually keep their distance from you. One additional benefit of stopping and dismounting from the bike is that it eliminates the very real risk of your having an accident if you continue trying to outrun the dog. Obviously this strategy involves some calculated risk, but many experienced touring cyclists think it's often the best strategy.

Carry non-lethal deterrents: Cyclists often like to carry protection with them to defend themselves against dogs that get too close. Effective dog deterrents come in a variety of forms. A **small air horn** is one approach. Dogs hate the sound and will often stop in their tracks when you blast an air horn in their direction. This is a good solution because it doesn't require precision in hitting the dog's face, as do sprays, and does no lasting harm to the dog.

Speaking of sprays, you can buy **commercial repellent sprays** such as pepper spray (where legal) that will stop most dogs in their tracks, or **make up a spray at home**, such as a squirt gun filled with water and vinegar. You can also buy animal-repellent sprays that work like pepper spray.

The problem with all sprays is your shooting accuracy (or lack thereof) while in a panicked state. Imagine an angry barking dog approaching you from behind while you are pedaling like a crazy person, with adrenaline pumping, trying to out-distance the dog. What do you think the odds are that you can successfully hit a dog's face with a spray in that scenario? It's worth a shot perhaps, but odds may be even greater that you will wreck your bike while racing ahead with one hand on the handlebars and one holding the spray bottle, while looking back at the angry dog. Seriously, that's a real risk. You don't want to focus so much on the dog that you lose control of your bike. That won't make for a happy ending.

A note on lethal deterrents: **Even if it is legal, I do not recommend carrying a loaded gun or any other potentially lethal weapons on your bike.** Some cyclists do so, but there are numerous drawbacks. First, you must deal with potential liability issues if you shoot someone's pet dog. No matter how ferocious the dog seemed when pursuing you, the dog's family and neighbors will all testify that the dog had a sweet disposition and never harmed anyone. Plus, if you shoot the wrong person's dog, he or she just might be angry enough to get in their car and give chase to you. That might not end well. Besides, depending on where you are riding, carrying a firearm may be illegal.

Admittedly, none of these "solutions" sound too promising. Dogs are unpredictable. For that reason, if you aren't comfortable dealing with dogs, what makes the most sense is to avoid putting yourself in situations where loose dogs are likely to be a problem. If you ride on bike trails or within parks, for instance, the chances of getting chased by an angry dog are very slim. If you ride inside a 55+ community or a nice residential neighborhood, you will likely be safe from truly dangerous dogs. From my experience, where you are most likely to encounter large, angry dogs is along rural highways and in certain urban areas where dogs are routinely allowed to run loose. Avoid these problem spots and you reduce your chances for such unpleasant encounters.

Coping With Troublesome People

Annoying or threatening people can show up most anywhere. If you get approached by a threatening person while cycling, you have a few options.

Don't go out solo: **Your best defense is to not ride alone.** As the saying goes, there is strength in numbers. Fair or not, it's an unfortunate fact that older people and women of all ages are oftentimes more vulnerable when walking or cycling solo. Sorry if that's not politically correct to say, but it's true. Your best defense may be to ride with a buddy or group.

Know when to ride: Avoiding cycling at night will also reduce your chances of encounters with criminal elements who want to rob or harm you. That's another reason not to ride after dark.

If you do encounter someone: First, you may be able to **avoid them.** If that's a possibility, simply do a u-turn when trouble lurks ahead and ride the other way. Avoiding trouble is always best. You may also be able to **outrun them**, especially with an electric bike. Not many people can run fast for very long. Odds are they will give up the chase soon.

Another approach is to **sound an alarm.** You can buy bike alarms, and many of them have remotes you can keep with you that include a panic button. This may not help if you are on a lonely trail out in the woods, but in urban areas or on busy trails, sounding a loud alarm will scare most intruders away.

Remember that **pepper spray** I mentioned for dogs? It works well on humans too. Just remember that as with any weapon, you may only get one chance to use it. If you aim pepper spray at someone, you'd better be prepared to use it quickly and with force. **If you carry pepper spray or something similar, be sure to keep it where you can access it quickly.** I keep my spray on my handlebars, attached with Velcro. It's always in sight and easy to reach. Don't bury it in a bike bag. In an emergency, it won't do you much good there.

Animals or humans, the safest options are to ride with a partner or group, and be careful where you ride.

Always Let Someone Know Where You Are

Many cyclists get great pleasure from going on long solo trail rides, sometimes riding anywhere from 20 to 60 miles per day. **If you are leaving home on your bike, be sure someone knows where you are going, including the name of the trail you plan to ride and its location.** Let them know where you parked your car and when you expect to be home. Always carry your well-charged cellphone, although in wilderness areas it may not work. If your cellphone includes a feature where someone else can track your location, be sure you have a spouse, partner, or friend connected to this service and that they know how to use it.

Wear Identification

The author wears a similar ID bracelet to offer himself and his wife additional peace of mind while he is riding.

One day while riding my bike solo and far from home, I started thinking about what would happen if I were incapacitated or worse while cycling. No one would have a clue who I was, where I lived, or who to contact. I realized that I needed to keep identification on me at all times when riding. Most of us don't cycle with bulky wallets and purses, where identification information is normally kept. **While you can carry ID in a bike handlebar bag or pannier, it's best to wear it.** One popular solution is an ID bracelet such as the ones sold by companies such as ROAD iD. These bracelets come in a variety of styles and colors, with your personalized identification information. Wearing this ID bracelet gives me (and my wife) more peace of mind.

Take a Bike Safety Class

You may think riding a bicycle is simple and requires no training. If nothing else, this chapter has hopefully taught you that cycling safely and successfully is sometimes not easy unless you are well informed. *To be a safe cyclist and to reduce your chances of accidents and injuries, you need to be well informed.* For this reason, many cycling groups offer bike-safety training classes. In the U.S., the League of American Bicyclists sponsors the Smart Cycling program, with classes offered nationwide by more than 3,000 certified instructors. Many 55+ communities, senior centers, and bike shops offer the League's Smart Cycling courses. It would be time well spent to enroll in these classes, or find an equivalent class wherever you may live. If your community doesn't offer a safe-cycling course for adults, consider getting certified and teaching it.

You Can Do This!

Everything we do in life carries some risk. *Don't let these risks keep you from pursuing your dreams and living your life,* whether that's cycling, hiking, fishing, traveling solo, hunting, scuba diving, horseback riding, or whatever your passion may be. Have the adventurous spirit of former U.S. President George H.W. Bush, who skydived from an airplane to celebrate his 90th birthday!

After reading this chapter, you are now equipped with all the information you need to enjoy a safe and enjoyable pastime riding your new e-bike or e-trike during your senior years. Follow these steps and you will significantly reduce your chances for accidents, injuries, and other challenges.

Riding an e-bike really is going to put the FUN back into cycling (and life), no matter what your age! There are plenty of adventures still awaiting ahead and new memories to make. You can do this!

Speaking of new adventures, in the Rider Profile that follows this chapter, you will learn how some seniors are using their e-bikes to explore the world and spend time with friends. Then, in Chapter 11, you will learn how to maintain and protect your new e-bike. 👓

Laura Maydahl

Enjoying Adventures in E-Bike Touring with Friends

"Every time we get on our bikes, I come home just feeling so much better about myself." - *Laura Maydahl*

The social aspect of cycling is part of the appeal for Laura Maydahl, 65, who is a fan of taking long, adventurous, multi-day group trips on her e-bike.

"Getting out and being with other folks and just visiting with them. It's another way to be social," Laura said of her experience since first purchasing an e-bike nearly five years ago.

Laura, who lives in San Juan Capistrano, California, said she was first introduced to e-bikes by participating in a "Sunday Funday" group bike ride sponsored by her local Pedego Electric Bikes store. Many local Pedego bike stores host group rides both as a benefit to existing bike owners and to introduce newcomers like Laura to their brand.

It only took one "Sunday Funday" group ride to convince Laura and her partner, Alice Kuchinskas, to join the e-bike movement.

"I turned to Alice and said 'this is crazy, this is way too much fun!'" Laura said, recalling her experience on that first two-hour group ride.

That first experience on an e-bike helped Laura overcome a challenge she had faced trying to ride a regular bike with a partner who was a more experienced cyclist.

"With my other half being an avid bicycle rider and me wanting to keep up with her, I couldn't keep up on a regular bike," Laura said. After that first group ride on rented e-bikes, both Laura and Alice bought Pedego e-bikes.

"This (e-bikes) levels the playing field tremendously," Laura said. "It's opened up a whole new way of being outside together."

With her new bike, Laura became a regular participant in the Sunday Funday rides, which were typically 30 to 35 miles in length and included a stop for lunch. She said she enjoyed the rides and making new friends through the group.

For Laura, far more ambitious group rides were soon to come. In the summer of 2018, a group of 20 senior riders from Southern California put their e-bikes in a van and drove to Pennsylvania, where they spent 10 days touring by bike on the Great Allegheny Passage (GAP) Trail, one of the nation's most popular long-distance bike trails. They rode 350 miles, staying in motels along the way.

"We were all at least in our 60s on that ride and we had a blast," Laura said.

The experience also gave Laura even more inspiration to keep cycling. She recalled the story of one woman on the trip who celebrated her 75th birthday while on the tour.

"She had had a heart attack four years previous and had two replaced knees. She can't walk a block, but she can ride her bike for miles."

Another rider on the GAP Trail tour also overcame health challenges through cycling.

"Another gal who was in her early 60s had had seven back surgeries," Laura said. "She can't walk very far at all without tremendous pain, but she can ride her bike as long as she wants on a given day."

The following summer a similar group from Southern California took their e-bikes to another famous long-distance trail, the Erie Canalway Trail in New York. Over 11 days, the group rode about 400 miles.

Laura's grandest trip yet happened in the summer of 2021, when Laura, Alice, and four other women took off in their RVs, with e-bikes on the back, from their California homes and trekked over 7,000 miles up the West Coast and as far east as Indiana. During the two-month journey, they rode on 10 bike trails for a total of 200 to 250 miles. Laura said their favorite cycling routes were the Mickelson Trail in South Dakota's Black Hills and the Discovery Trail in Long Beach, Washington.

Laura said she's sold on the benefits of cycling, and especially e-bikes, for helping senior adults stay active and enjoy their retirement years.

"They (seniors) realize they need to continue to stay active and mobile, and this is a very really low-impact way to do that. For us, every time we get on our bikes, I come home just feeling so much better about myself. It's been a game-changer for us." 👓

_"I think the e-bike has saved my life.
As long as I can ride, I will."_

KEITH PEGG (PAGE 9)

CHAPTER 11

The Care and Feeding of an E-Bike; Maintenance Tips You Need to Know

"I love riding my bike for the sense of freedom it gives a person. I can ride down the street or across the country. The same feelings you had when you first rode a bike as a kid."

- Frank Cauthorn, long-distance bike touring and adventurer

"Be at one with the universe. If you can't do that, at least be at one with your bike."

- Leonard Zinn

Buying an electric bike or trike is one of the best decisions you can make as an active senior adult, but it's not an inexpensive one. If you're going to invest a few thousand dollars in buying one or more e-bikes or e-trikes, it pays to know how to properly maintain and protect them. That's the topic of this chapter and the next one.

Happily, bicycles are relatively simple and straightforward machines. Even a decent-quality bike with proper maintenance will give years of good service and mostly trouble-free riding. Taking time to properly maintain your new e-bike will make it ride better and last longer, with fewer shop visits.

Here are some suggestions for maintaining your pride and joy, your new electric bike.

Get an Annual Bike Check-Up: Lots of us get an annual physical exam from our doctors, even if we're feeling fine. Your e-bike will appreciate the same consideration. Take your bike to a local bike store at least once a year for a tune-up and inspection. If you are a high-mileage rider, you may need more frequent tune-ups. Even if you bought your bike online, many local bike stores (but not all) will do servicing and repair work on your bike. In this chapter, we're going to give you plenty of tips for maintaining your bike at home, but even so, few of us are trained bike mechanics. The bike store staff will know exactly what to do to keep your bike in top shape. They will inspect for worn parts and answer your questions about your bike, including that "funny squeaking sound" you can't seem to find.

Properly Store It: It's not good for any bicycle to be left outdoors in the elements, but e-bikes have electronic parts that make them even more sensitive to weather. If you want your bike to continue to look good and perform well, you need to store it in an enclosed area away from rain, snow, high humidity, and too much direct sunlight. A garage or shed is ideal, unless of course you can convince your spouse or partner to let you keep your bike inside the apartment or house. Good luck with that one! Can't keep the entire bike inside the house? At least make it a habit to remove the battery each night and bring it indoors, especially during hot or cold weather or if you live in an area with high humidity or salty air. (Later in this chapter, we will provide more tips on maintaining your bike's battery).

Say 'No' to Dirt: Bikes don't like dirt and grime. One of the most critical components to keep clean is the bike chain, along with the cassette (gear sprockets), and related moving parts of the drivetrain. It's a simple but slightly messy job.

How often you need to clean the chain depends on how much and where you ride. If you mostly ride on clean, paved streets and trails, and don't put excessive mileage on your bike, then giving your chain and drivetrain a good cleaning every three months may be adequate. If you ride on dusty or muddy trails often or take your bike on the beach, you will need more frequent cleanings; more information about caring for e-bikes that you ride on the beach is addressed on page 187.

- ⚙ **To clean the drivetrain,** first use a chain degreaser (spray or liquid) to clean the chain and cassette. Use an old toothbrush or wire brush to carefully clean the chain and cassette after each step, removing dirt and debris. A cloth rag is good for wiping down the chain and removing any remaining grit and degreaser residue.

- ⚙ If necessary, **rinse** with a modest amount of water – hot if available – but do so very carefully.

- ⚙ **WARNING: <u>Never</u> use a high-pressure hose or a high-force garden hose nozzle when cleaning an e-bike and <u>never</u> point the water at electronic parts.** Some manufacturers warn to not use water at all when cleaning your bike.

- ⚙ It's a good idea to read (and heed) your bike's owner's manual for model-specific cleaning suggestions. **For the chain and cassette**, however, it should be safe to carefully rinse them with water to remove any remaining dirt or grease before finishing the job. If you don't ride through mud or on the beach, you may be able to skip this step and avoid using water. Wipe excess moisture off the chain, cassette, and other parts. Let the bike dry.

- ⚙ The job isn't finished until you **lubricate your chain and drivetrain**; instructions for doing so are in the next section. If you need to clean your chain frequently or take care of several bicycles, you may want to invest in a chain-cleaning tool. Ask your bike shop for suggestions.

- ⚙ For **cleaning the rest of the bike**, a damp cloth and a mild cleaning soap, when needed, should be sufficient. Again, it's not recommended to use a garden hose or pressure washer on your e-bike due to the electronic components. Taking extra care to wipe down the wheels and handlebars will keep them looking new longer.

⚙ For **brake rotors**, clean them only with a damp cloth, rubbing alcohol, or automotive brake-cleaning fluid. Never put any wax or lubricants on the brake rotors or pads. (See below for more instructions about caring for e-bike brakes).

Lubrication Works Wonders. Once you have cleaned the chain, it is important to lubricate it right away. A dry chain will often develop an annoying squealing noise, won't perform as smoothly, and over time may rust. Apply a lubricant specially formulated for bike chains. **Do not use household products such as standard WD-40, which is a cleaner, not a lubricant, and is not designed for use on bike chains.** It's important to pick the right formulation of chain lubricant for your bike, based on the climate where you ride, whether it is dry or humid. By the way, since I mentioned the WD-40 brand name, it's only fair to add that they make a special WD-40 bike lubricant. That one is OK to use. To get the best product for your bike and climate, ask your local bike shop for recommendations.

The chain isn't the only part of the bike that needs periodic lubricating. Your bike has several wire cables, all of which need lubrication to work smoothly and resist rust. Pulleys and other moving parts on the gears' derailleur also need bike lubricant, but make sure they are clean first.

When you purchase a new e-bike, it's always a good idea to review the owner's manual, which these days is often only available online. Look at the maintenance section. Pay special attention to what the manual says about cleaning and lubricating. It may tell you which parts to lubricate and what types of lubricants are best.

*A **Word about Riding on the Beach:*** Perhaps the harshest environment of all for riding an e-bike is on the beach. That's a shame because riding an e-bike on the beach is tons of fun. The "fat tire" e-bikes with 4-inch-wide tires and plenty of treads are perfect for riding on hard-packed sandy beaches. An e-bike motor makes cruising through sand much easier too. Still, if you care about your bike and plan to keep it for a reasonably long period of time, riding on the beach isn't a great idea.

Beaches are one of the most fun – and most harsh – places to ride an e-bike, requiring extra care during and after. Never ride your e-bike in the water itself, no matter how shallow, and be prepared to clean and lubricate the e-bike after every beachfront ride.

If you do take your e-bike on the beach, never ride it through salty water, such as at the ocean's edge. After riding on the beach, be prepared to do a thorough cleaning. Yes, you will need to do this cleaning routine after every ride. **Clean the chain and drive chain, lubricate the chain and cables, and wipe down the entire bike with a damp cloth. This routine will help slow down the corrosive effect of salt and sand but unfortunately won't stop it.** No matter how well you care for your e-bike after each ride, the harsh reality is that riding it on the beach is going to mean more frequent trips to the bike shop, more parts to replace, and a shorter lifespan for the bike.

Regardless, I know many of you will still want to ride your e-bike on the beach. I've done it too, so I understand. It's a blast to ride along the beach. Beyond the extra cleaning regimen suggested above, here are two more suggestions for those of us who who can't resist the allure of beach bike riding.

If you are an infrequent visitor to the beach, maybe just going there on vacation or holiday, consider renting an e-bike for the beach,

rather than taking your own bike. Bike shop owners in beach areas understand how to maintain their bikes and build the extra wear and tear into the rental price. **However, if you live near the beach or plan to ride there frequently, consider buying a second e-bike that is primarily for beach use.** Buy a cheaper model, one with the tire size and configuration that best suits the beach. You will still need to follow the stepped-up cleaning regimen described above, but subjecting a cheaper bike to these harsh elements and understanding the consequences sure beats ruining your finely engineered $5,000 brand-name e-bike by pedaling it across the sand.

Maintain Proper Tire Pressure. Just like in a car, truck, or motorcycle, the tires on an e-bike are critically important to your safety, performance, and comfort. **Make sure you know the correct tire pressure for your e-bike, usually expressed as pounds per square inch, or psi.** Tire pressure levels vary greatly depending on the type of tires your bike has. Mountain bikes and fat-tire e-bikes and trikes carry relatively low pressure (30 to 40 psi) to absorb shock and provide a smoother ride. Cruiser-style and hybrid bikes, the most popular style for seniors, often require 50 to 70 psi for a smooth but responsive ride. Road (racing-style) bikes with those ultra-skinny tires run at high pressure, in the range of 80 to 130 psi, to reduce drag and allow higher speeds.

Check your tires' pressure before each ride, at least with a quick thumb check. That's not an accurate guide to exact tire pressure, but it will warn you if your tire is dangerously low on air. Periodically, typically weekly or monthly, you need to check air pressure with a gauge and add air as necessary. Bike tires, especially those that run at higher pressure, naturally lose air over time, whether ridden or not.

Every bicyclist needs to own one or more hand-held pumps and know how to use them. Using a hand-held air pump, however, isn't always easy for some seniors and those with disabilities.

The pumping motion required to fill bike tires can be exhausting. Fortunately, modern technology has solutions you may want to consider. CO2 air cartridges are popular with many cyclists and readily available at bike shops, sporting goods stores, and online. They are small, lightweight, and not expensive. My favorite tech solution is a small portable air compressor, powered by a rechargeable lithium battery and equipped with an LED screen readout. These miniature pumps make filling bike tires easy and they have good accuracy. They are small enough to carry in your bike bag. Just be sure to keep them charged.

How to Cope with Flat Tires

One of the more annoying realities of bike riding is that bike tires and tubes are easily punctured, resulting in flat tires. Unlike cars and trucks, the rubber on bike tires is thin and the tires carry higher air pressure. Most bike tires still have tubes, something that was common on cars and trucks in the first half of the 20th century.

Other than buying tubeless tires, which has its own pros and cons, you can't totally protect yourself from getting flats. There are, however, steps you can take to minimize the chances of a flat tire. First, **look for tires that come with Kevlar linings or something similar.** Kevlar is the same tough material from which bullet-proof vests are made. Some bike tires come with Kevlar lining, but if yours does not ask your bike shop about adding a liner. This provides a barrier of protection between your tires and their tubes. Cheaper-quality tires are more likely to get flats. If you are buying a low-cost electric bike, you may want to consider upgrading to better tires with liners.

Another popular technique is to **add a gooey substance to your tires that will quickly close up small punctures** and help you avoid getting a flat tire. There are several products on the market, with two of the more popular ones being Slime and Flat Out. They are simple to add to your tires, won't affect your bike's performance, and won't require any additional maintenance once installed. Slime, Flat Out, and similar products are very effective at filling small punctures but won't protect you from punctures caused by large shards of glass or other larger cuts. Cyclists tend to either love or hate products like Slime. They significantly reduce your odds of getting flats, but the substance is quite messy when you're changing a tire and can clog tire valves.

Did you ever use Fix-A-Flat to temporarily refill a car's tire? You can use a similar product to fix a bike's flat tire while on the road if you don't want to bother with fixing it the more traditional way. A Fix-A-Flat-type product comes in a small spray can that is designed to do what Slime does and at the same time refill the air in your tire. Fix-A-Flat makes a version for bikes, but the most popular product in this category for bikes is GUP.

If you are handy, you can go the more traditional route and **carry a tube repair kit and a pump.** Fixing a flat yourself isn't usually that hard. You can watch YouTube videos to learn how to change a bike's flat tire. True cycling enthusiasts think everyone who rides a bike should know how to fix a flat. Maybe they are right. However, since e-bikes are heavy, turning one upside down to change a flat may be beyond the capabilities of many Baby Boomers. Plus, if you're like me, flats only happen when the weather is extremely hot (or cold) and a thunderstorm is approaching. You may not want to take time to fix your bike along the side of the road.

One caution when fixing a flat tire is that *small bike pumps that you are likely to carry on your bicycle are notoriously slow at refilling a tire's air.* You are going to pump it up and down dozens of times for several minutes to get sufficient air pressure, something that isn't fun on a hot or rainy day or if you aren't in the best of physical conditioning. Thankfully, there are modern alternatives to the bike pump like the CO2 canisters and small portable air compressors powered by lithium batteries. Be sure you have one or more of these tools with you at all times in your bike's bag.

Your best bet is to ride carefully and avoid areas with broken glass. Buy good-quality tires that have a Kevlar lining, and maybe consider the added protection offered by products such as Slime or Flat Out. This will minimize your chances of getting flats. In the event you do get a flat tire, carry a GUP or similar spray can with you. Once you are back home, take your bike to a shop to get the tube replaced.

E-Bike Brake Maintenance

Just like on your car or truck, **disc brakes on your e-bike require occasional maintenance and repairs.** One of the more common issues is with brake pads wearing out and needing to be replaced. If you are a reasonably handy do-it-yourself type person, replacing brake pads is an easy and inexpensive repair. Most e-bike owners, however, will want to take their bikes to a bike shop when brake pads wear thin and need replacement.

A telltale sign that your brake pads need attention is when they begin to make a grinding noise, or when the brake levers on the handlebars travel too far when you apply the brakes. **Worn brake pads need attention promptly because continuing to ride the bike when brake pads are grinding could damage the rotors.** It's a good idea to have a bike shop mechanic do a thorough checkup on your e-bike periodically, perhaps annually, and that checkup should include taking a look at the brakes.

If you notice a new squealing noise when applying the brakes, sometimes quite loud, it may be the brake rotors that need attention, not the pads. Rotors often get road film or other grime on them and need a good cleaning. In some cases, a thin coat of road grime on the rotors is not even noticeable to the human eye, but it will affect our brakes' performance. Cleaning the rotors is a good do-it-yourself task you can do at home. You can use a clean cloth to apply the same brake-cleaning fluid or spray you use on your car's brakes, which is readily available at auto parts stores. You can also use isopropyl alcohol or other cleaning solvents. **Never use an oil- or wax-based solvent on brake rotors.** If the squeal continues after this cleaning, the pads may need cleaning or replacing.

Caring for Your E-Bike Battery

The battery is not only one of the most important, but also the most expensive, of all e-bike components. For these reasons, it pays to take good care of it.

E-bike batteries are finicky. They don't like extreme weather, hot or cold. If you store your e-bike in a garage, shed, or other spot exposed to high heat, humidity, or winter cold, it is best to remove the battery after riding and keep it indoors. It's also best to remove the battery before transporting your e-bike on a bike rack on the back of your vehicle. It's not only potentially exposed to rain and either hot or cold weather while on the bike rack, but e-bike batteries are a tempting target for thieves. Nor should you leave an e-bike battery for prolonged periods of time inside your car (or trunk) during summer heat.

Similar to the debate about cellphone batteries, there is considerable disagreement about the best strategy to keep your e-bike battery charged, both while using it and when it is in storage or out of season. Following good charging practices can affect your battery's performance and longevity. Read the manufacturer's instructions and follow them, or talk with the pros at the bike shop where you bought the bike. As a general rule, you should not allow a lithium battery to run all the way down or stay uncharged. Don't let your battery fall below 25 percent charged. If you are not riding the e-bike for a few months, perhaps due to winter weather, extended travel, or while you recover from a serious illness, it's important to store it fully charged and remember to periodically re-charge your bike's battery. Batteries differ, but as a general rule checking the charge status once a month while in storage should be sufficient.

Take good care of your bike's battery and it will serve you well for several years of average use.

Your E-Bike Will Thank You

Following the recommendations in this chapter will keep your e-bike running well and looking good for many years. As you will soon learn, your e-bike will hold a special place in your heart. It will change your life for the better. You are going to have FUN cycling again! For these reasons, **the time you spend learning to properly care for your e-bike will be time well spent.**

In the next chapter, we will share tips on an equally important subject: how to protect your e-bike in all circumstances. Among other things, you will learn how to reduce your chances of becoming a victim of bike thieves!

The Rider Profile that follows this chapter is a fascinating story of how one senior overcame major obstacles and got her health and life back thanks to her electric trike. 👓

RIDER PROFILE
Linda Heiland
Getting Her Life Back Thanks to an Electric Trike

"E-bikes really are the best kind of medicine!"

When she was younger, Linda Heiland was quite athletic, participating in competitive roller skating, rock climbing, and breaking horses, among other pursuits. As she grew older, serious health problems began to emerge, including degenerative bone disease, arthritis, and advanced osteoporosis. Exercise became difficult and she began to gain weight.

"The problem with being able to lose weight is that if you are in constant pain and you are unable to exercise, everything is exacerbated," said Linda, now 63.

As time went on, Linda required a complete knee replacement and later a hip replacement that resulted in complications. To make matters worse, back problems began in 2018.

"I spent over 18 months basically bedridden and either on a walker or in a wheelchair between 10 surgeries and other procedures. Eighteen months of no activity had just about ended me and my marriage. I

194

could not do anything. I was in constant unremitting pain. I owned my own consulting business and was unable to work. The business that I had spent eight years building was wiped out in a matter of months."

That's when Linda and her husband Leo who live in Chandler, Arizona, discovered e-bikes. Some friends purchased e-bikes and suggested Leo and Linda consider them. Given her poor balance due to her back and hip problems, Linda opted for an electric trike, with three wheels, instead of an e-bike. Leo bought an e-bike.

"I started slow, only one or two miles for the first couple of days," Linda recalled. "I was determined that I would push myself and add a little more on my rides each day. Now, just a few short months later and the results are unbelievable. I ride between 13 and 15 miles daily. I have lost 41 pounds and I can stand upright and walk now. My stamina is amazingly better. I'm able to cook and do simple household tasks again for the first time in almost two years."

For Linda, her e-trike has been life changing.

"I credit my trike with giving us our lives back. It is night and day from where I was two years ago. Our friends are in awe of the changes in my health and general well-being. (E-bikes) really are the best kind of medicine!"

Leo is a retired product safety engineer and helped the couple research e-bikes. He's become quite knowledgeable about the bikes and how they work. He rides an Evelo Delta X e-bike and Linda rides an Evelo Compass e-trike.

"We are planning biking trips for the future and new riding trails near where we live," Linda said. **"Life is fun again."** 👓

CHAPTER 12

How to Protect Your E-Bike Investment

"To me, it doesn't matter whether it's raining or the sun is shining or whatever: as long as I'm riding a bike I know I'm the luckiest guy in the world."

- Mark Cavendish, British professional bicycle racer

An electric bike is much more than just a financial investment. It's an investment in your health and happiness. Because your new e-bike will become such an integral part of your life and identity, there are additional steps you need to take to keep it (and you) safe.

Unfortunately, when you have something of real value like an e-bike, someone is going to try to take it. **Bike thefts are on the rise worldwide as biking grows in popularity.** E-bikes are prime targets because of their high cost, high demand, and short supply. According to UK bike insurer Bikmo, bike thefts are rising at high double-digit rates. New York City police officers report that bike thefts rose 27 percent during a recent reporting period compared with the same period a year ago. Follow these tips to reduce your chances of becoming a bike-theft victim!

Secure Storage

Previously in this book, I discussed the benefits of **storing your e-bike either inside your home or apartment (best), or in a garage or shed.** That helps keep the bike cleaner and safely away from the harmful effects of direct sunlight, rain, and snow. Another benefit of storing your e-bike in an enclosed, lockable area is security. Your bike is much less likely to be stolen from your home if it is indoors or in a secured shelter. Cheap department-store bikes from years past may have been OK to leave in an exposed carport, locked overnight to an outside bike rack, or in other highly visible spots, but not your prized e-bike. Sophisticated thieves know that e-bikes have value and are easy to sell on the black market. Find a secure place to store your bikes.

Garage: A garage is only secure when the door is shut. Many people are in the habit of leaving their garage door open during the day. Did you know that criminals actually cruise streets and alleys to look for open garage doors and potential merchandise to plunder? An open garage door is an invitation for someone to come take your stuff, so **keep your garage door shut whenever you are not coming or going from it.**

Carport: If you must leave your beautiful new e-bike locked on a carport, in a parking garage, or similar exposed location, you can improve your odds against theft by **covering it with a bike cover to reduce its visibility.** A good cover will also protect the bike from dust, rain, and sunlight. (See our recommendations about bike locks later in this chapter).

Take your power back: Another step to protect the bike is to **remove the battery and take it indoors.** It's not only good for the battery to be in a temperature-and-humidity controlled environment but an e-bike without its battery is less of a target for thieves. If the carport or other outdoor area is at your private residence, install a motion-detector flood light that will brightly light up the carport if an intruder enters it at night.

Keep an eye out: **Installing a security camera pointed toward your**

bike is another smart security idea if your bike stays outdoors, such as under a carport or in a driveway. A security "cam" can help identify anyone who enters the carport or driveway and gets too close to your bike. With today's technology, the security camera can easily be set up to give you an alert on your cellphone whenever someone enters your protected zone. You may not want to confront a thief, but getting the alert on your phone would give you time to call the police or set off any alarms you may have to scare the thief away.

Bike Locks and Alarms

Physical locks and deterrent alarms are important tools in keeping your bike safe. They will improve your chances against bike thieves. Let's take a deeper look at locks and alarms.

Bike Locks: No one should ride a bike without at least one good bike lock and preferably two. If you are buying an e-bike or trike, be sure to invest right away in good-quality locks. Ask your bike shop for recommendations on locks. Getting the right (best) lock for your needs is an important decision.

Bike locks come in a variety of types and prices. Some are better than others, but none of them will prevent a determined and skilled thief from stealing your bike if he has the right tools and opportunity.

When buying bike locks, two key factors are weight and price. Some of the toughest bike locks are quite heavy, weighing as much or more than your e-bike's battery. These may be OK for home use but are not well suited for carrying with you on bike rides. You may need to compromise on quality in order to get a lock that is light enough to carry with you.

When it comes to price, top-rated locks often sell for $125 or more.

Even if that is too expensive for your budget, don't make the mistake of going to the opposite extreme and buying the cheapest locks. They will do a poor job of protecting your bike, so what good are they? Spend as much money as you can to get the best locks your budget can afford.

British product-testing firm Sold Secure offers a widely used rating system for bike locks that runs from Bronze (lowest protection) to Diamond (best protection). Relatively few locks earn the Diamond rating, but you should be able to find suitable Silver and Gold-rated ones. Another popular rating service is the Dutch firm ART. It rates locks on a scale of 1 to 5, with 5 being the most secure.

Cable locks are recommended for backup, not as a primary locking device. Author's photo.

Here is a closer look at the major types of bike locks:

Cable locks are one of the most common styles, probably because of their low price. Unfortunately, they are also the lowest-quality type of bike lock. Any average thief can quickly cut a cable lock. **Don't bother with cable locks unless you use them as a secondary lock**, and even then they aren't always the best choice.

Chain locks are more secure, but may be too heavy to carry while riding. Author's photo.

Top-rated *chain locks* are among the most secure bike locks, but also the heaviest, so carrying one of the heavier chain locks with you on a bike ride may not be practical. They are too heavy to carry in a backpack and don't mount easily to a bike's frame. Some cyclists will wear the chain lock around their waist like a belt, but that's not a fashion statement most of us senior adults want to make. One warning with chain locks is that they are not all created equal. The toughness of the chain's material and its weight are going to determine how effective it is as a theft deterrent. An inexpensive chain lock may be only slightly better than a good cable lock. Mid-quality chain locks, however, can be an excellent choice, either for a primary lock in a relatively low-crime, reasonably safe setting, or as a tough secondary lock. Mid-range chain locks are not as heavy and may be easier to carry on your bike.

Two of the better types of bike locks to carry with you on your bike are **U-lock (also called D-lock)** and **folding locks.** A high-quality U-lock is a difficult target for thieves. Like the top-rated chain locks, the best U-locks are also quite heavy. While they offer excellent protection, U-locks are rigid steel locks that can be hard to wrap

A U-Lock or D-Lock engaged with the e-bike and a post. Used by Permission of Seatylock.

around your bike's frame and a nearby post or bike rack. Despite their hefty weight and inflexibility, U-locks are favored by many cyclists as an excellent primary lock. Many of them come with mounting hardware so you can carry the lock on the bike's frame.

Folding locks are a newer category that is gaining in popularity. Folding locks are made of tough steel similar to U-locks. Unlike U-locks, folding locks have flexible parts that make them easier to fit around frames and the nearest stationary object. When folded, folding locks are compact

A folding lock keeps the strength of steel, but is easier to manipulate into different shapes. Used by Permission of Seatylock.

and easy to mount or carry on your bike. They make a good choice for a primary or secondary bike lock.

In recent years, many new innovations in bike locks have begun to emerge. **Bike security is a subject that is changing quickly.** State-of-the-art protection today may be out of date in a few years. Some of these innovations involve technology and the use of built-in alarms. Some bike manufacturers are introducing new built-in locks and security devices for their e-bikes, reducing the need to buy after-market products. It will be interesting to see which new technologies and styles emerge as winners in the near future.

Best Practices for Bike Security

Multiple, sturdy locking devices: As already mentioned, **the best defensive strategy is to use two locks, preferably different types.** This will require more time and effort for would-be thieves to steal your bike, which will likely discourage them from trying. It's also advantageous to mount the lock as low on the bike as possible, in a tight spot with not much slack. This practice makes it more difficult for the thief to use tools to cut your lock.

Whichever lock, or combination of locks, seems best for your needs and budget, be sure to make bike security a priority. When it comes to keeping your bike secure from thieves, remember you don't necessarily always have to use the very best locks and technology; you just need better locks than some of the other bikes parked near yours! Thieves are lazy and will pick the easiest target to steal.

Stay in the light: Another good practice, combined with multiple sturdy locks, is to **park your bike in a high-visibility or well-lit public area.** Thieves prefer darker spots and out-of-the-way locations where they can work without being noticed.

Alarms and Trackers: It won't take the place of good locks, but one relatively inexpensive way to protect your e-bike is to **add a motion-**

detector alarm. Selling as inexpensively as $20, these alarms attach to your bike and are activated through a remote control. If someone touches your bike, it will sound a loud alarm. That is enough to make most would-be thieves quickly walk away for fear of being caught. Some of these alarms include lights or horns, making them even more useful. Another option is to add a GPS tracker. This will show your bike's location, no matter where it is, allowing police to recover it. The downside of GPS trackers is that some of them are relatively expensive and many GPS trackers require a monthly or annual subscription fee.

Register Your E-Bike: It is a good idea to register your bike so the make, model, and serial number will be on file with police departments. This won't prevent a theft but may help you recover your bike later. Bike Index, the largest bike registry organization, says more than 9,300 registered bikes have been recovered by their owners, thanks to the registry. Another popular registry in the U.S. is BikeGuard. It claims that a bike is stolen every seven seconds in the U.S. In the UK, BikeRegister claims that more than 1 million bikes are registered with it. Most registries are free to use and all of them work closely with local and state police departments to help identify and return stolen bikes. It's a simple process to register, so I recommend this step for everyone who owns an e-bike.

Insure Your E-Bike: Many e-bike owners have learned the hard way that their **homeowners, renters, or automotive insurance policies do not cover e-bikes, or at least don't provide comprehensive coverage.**

If you call to ask, your insurance agent may assure you that your e-bike is covered. Don't be too quick to believe it. Ask to see it in writing. Your agent may be assuming that since their policies cover bicycles then e-bikes would surely be included too. Don't count on it. Some companies do, but most do not. Their underwriters make a distinction between traditional bikes and e-bikes because e-bikes have motors and are capable of higher average speeds.

You may need a separate e-bike insurance policy for a variety of reasons. The obvious one is to protect you in case of theft. Another reason is coverage for damage to your bike in the event of an accident. A third reason is liability coverage to protect you in the event that you cause an accident that injures or otherwise harms another person.

Even if your existing homeowners or renters insurance has some coverage for your e-bike, it is probably limited. For example, does it offer full-replacement cost coverage if your bike is stolen or destroyed in an accident? Probably not. Unless your existing policies provide full and comprehensive coverage for your e-bike, you would be wise to obtain a separate e-bike insurance policy.

In the U.S., several insurers offer e-bike coverage, including Velosurance, Markel, SPOKE, Sundays Insurance, and Simple Bike Insurance. In Canada, providers include The Co-operators Insurance Co., Pedal Power Insurance, Think Insure, Aviva, and Velosurance. The UK has numerous e-bike insurance providers. The list includes Velosure, Bikmo, CyclePlan, Bikesure, PedalCover, and PedalSure. These lists are not comprehensive of all available e-bike insurers in these countries and are not intended as an endorsement of any specific insurer.

An added bonus with e-bike insurance policies is that most of them include (or offer) roadside assistance. If your e-bike breaks down on a trail or road far from home, or you are involved in an accident that damages the bike, they will send someone to pick you up.

Transporting E-Bikes Safely

Owning an e-bike opens up all sorts of new opportunities for exploration and adventure! There's a whole world of trails, parks, and cycling tours awaiting you. You won't likely be content very long to only ride your e-bike around your neighborhood.

This brings up the question of how best to take your e-bike places using your personal vehicle or RV.

Rear-mounted e-bike rack: The most common solution is a bike rack, attached to the rear of your vehicle with a trailer hitch. **Since e-bikes are considerably heavier than regular bicycles, a bike rack you may have owned in the past won't work; nor will a lighter-weight bike rack attached to the trunk or hatchback of your car with straps and hooks. You are going to need a hitch-mounted rack made for electric bikes.**

First-time e-bike buyers are often shocked by what it costs to buy and install a trailer hitch and then buy a suitable e-bike rack. While you might find an e-bike rack as low as $300, most of the better-rated ones are in the range of $500 to $800. That's not counting the cost of the hitch and installation, if you don't already have one on your vehicle. Most e-bike racks will hold two e-bikes; some will hold even more.

Expensive or not, there are few other options for the typical passenger car. **You must have an e-bike rack to transport your bike (or bikes) safely on the back of your vehicle.** Considering the investment you're making in the e-bike, you don't want to cut corners with the rack. You need one that is easy to use, durable, and will safely carry your e-bike. Get the best e-bike rack you can afford.

In the cabin: **If your vehicle is a minivan, a larger SUV, or an RV, you may be able to skip buying an e-bike rack and carry your bike inside the vehicle.** In addition to saving on the cost of a rack, keeping your e-bike inside the vehicle protects it from theft, dirt, and harsh weather. Full-size e-bikes, however, won't be easy to slide into the back of a minivan or SUV, especially if you have two e-bikes to carry together. It will require some muscle strength to do so. You may also have to partially disassemble the bike to get it into your car, which is a hassle. This is why many seniors who travel frequently are buying smaller, folding e-bikes. When folded, these bikes will fit neatly into most vehicles. Where allowed, you can even carry them onto public transportation such as trains, subways, ferries, and buses.

Enclosed trailers: Another alternative for traveling with your e-bikes that doubles as security *and* storage is to use an **enclosed trailer that you haul behind your car, truck, or RV.** This works especially well if carrying multiple e-bikes or with e-trikes, which are harder to transport due to their larger size. An enclosed trailer keeps your bikes more secure from theft and safe from bad weather. With an enclosed trailer, you won't need to fret over bringing your bikes inside the hotel at night. Plus, this gives you extra space for hauling other items and keeping them locked up. If you only travel occasionally, you can rent enclosed trailers from stores such as U-Haul. You will, however, need a trailer hitch on your vehicle to haul a trailer.

Don't forget to lock up: When you travel using an e-bike rack, be sure to keep your bike securely locked to the rack and keep the rack locked to the trailer hitch. Always secure the bike well. Remove the battery before installing the bike on the rack. Cover battery terminals and other sensitive electronic parts if there is any chance of rain along the route. When parking at restaurants, truck stops, and rest stops, park in a busy spot that will discourage thieves and keep a good eye on your bike.

What To Do When Staying at a Hotel

This brings up another challenge that cyclists face when carrying their e-bikes on a vehicle's bike rack. **Should you bring your e-bikes inside the hotel each evening? The quick answer is yes.** In nearly all circumstances, it's better to bring your e-bike inside. Remember, bikes are popular targets for thieves, and high-value e-bikes are the grand prize. After you've done it a time or two, it only takes a few minutes to undo the locks and straps, remove your bike from the rack, and roll it into the hotel. Trust me, you will sleep better at night with your bike inside the room with you. The added peace of mind is well worth the extra work.

Not every hotel is going to be keen on letting you bring your bicycle inside. **Two suggestions that have worked well for my wife and me are to (1) Look for one of the older roadside motels where you can park right outside your room and not have to wheel your bike past the front desk or along long corridors, or (2) Ask for a ground-floor room and look for a place to park near the side entrance.** It's best to avoid having to take your bike into an elevator, although with most bikes you can carry them on an elevator if necessary.

Should you ask the hotel ahead of time about its policy on bringing bikes inside? Most hotels are OK with it. For this reason, my practice is to simply do it, assuming it is fine. You can always ask for forgiveness later if they object. I have never had a hotel complain about it.

Out of respect to the hotel, **do make sure your bike is clean and not dripping grease.** It's not usually necessary, but if you are concerned about soiling the hotel room's flooring, carry some butcher paper, a tarp, or cardboard to put your bike on in the room. Unless you are a mountain bike rider or just returned from a day at the beach with your bike, odds are it is clean enough to not do any harm to the hotel room.

Your E-Bike Deserves the Best Protection

There's no worse feeling for a cyclist than coming back to where you left your bike locked to a post or rack before lunch and finding it gone. Don't let it happen to you. **Take the time to follow the steps in this chapter and you can protect your bike against most thieves.** You can also protect yourself in the event your bike gets stolen anyway, despite your best efforts. You and your bike deserve the best protection possible.

In our final Rider Profile, we will look at one couple who overcame serious health challenges with the help of their e-bikes. 👓

Rodger and Claudia Price

*How an E-Trike Got This
Senior Couple Outdoors Again*

"E-bikes are the wave of the future."
– Claudia Price

You might think that bike riding would not be too appealing to an 80-year-old with a partial leg amputation. But don't tell that to Rodger Price. For him, an electric trike has made a world of difference, keeping him outdoors, active, and enjoying life.

"We weren't able to do hardly anything anymore," his wife, Claudia Price, 78, said about the years before Rodger bought his e-trike four years ago. "He cannot walk very far, but boy can he ride! We used to ski and we can't do that anymore. This (e-bike) is the only thing now that we can do together."

Biking had long been an activity Rodger and Claudia enjoyed. Claudia said she used to ride her bike to work in the summers. When she lived in Pennsylvania, she would sometimes ride 20 miles to a friend's house.

After Rodger's amputation in 1998, however, their days of riding together appeared to be over. He struggled for a while with riding a two-wheel bike, but with a prosthesis it just wasn't working well. Then, nearly five years ago, he discovered electric-powered recumbent trikes, a three-wheel bike with a low center of gravity and comfortable seating position.

"The recumbents are so much more comfortable," Rodger said. "The recumbent seat is like sitting at the kitchen table seat; it's a regular seat and a lot more comfortable."

Thanks to e-bikes, cycling once again plays an important role in Rodger and Claudia's lives. When the weather is good where they live in Fort Collins, Colorado, riding is part of their daily routine together.

"When it's summer, we're out almost every day," Claudia said. "We try to get at least 20 miles in (per day). The longest we've ridden is 42 miles and that was to Greeley (Colorado) and back."

The couple often spends winters at an RV resort in Mesa, Arizona, and when they do, the bikes go with them. They belong to three separate bike groups there.

Even for Claudia, e-bikes have made a real difference. She can now ride to a grocery store that is about two miles away, downhill, where riding home used to be a real challenge.

"I love my e-bike so much. I can get up and down the hills. Now I can go anywhere I want."

Rodger rides a Catrike brand electric trike. Claudia rides a Specialized Como e-bike.

"I think e-bikes are the wave of the future," Claudia said. 👓

Conclusion

If you are new to the wonderful world of electric bicycles, I hope this book has inspired you to give it a try. A good first step is to rent an e-bike for an hour or a day and go take a ride on a bike trail or through a low-traffic park or neighborhood. If you are like most first-time riders, you are going to return with a big grin on your face and eager to start shopping for your own e-bike. Nearly everyone who tries e-bikes likes them, especially if they ride long enough to get over any initial jitters and wobbles.

For those of you who are more experienced with riding e-bikes, I hope this book has provided you with a better understanding of your bike and the role of cycling in our world today. You are now armed with the information you need to more safely ride your e-bike and to properly maintain and protect it.

E-bikes are not a flash-in-the-pan fad. They are going to be with us for a long time. Sales will continue to climb. **Electric bikes will play an increasingly important role not only for recreation and exercise, but for meeting basic transportation needs, helping resolve urban traffic congestion, and as a "green" alternative for fighting harmful climate change.** Bike infrastructure, such as bike trails and bike lanes, will continue to expand, making riding safer and more enjoyable.

For senior adults and those of any age with health challenges, e-bikes are truly life-changing. They improve the quality of life for those who ride them, adding to their health and happiness. They are one of the most significant new product developments for seniors in a long time.

Thank you for taking time to read this book. As you begin (or expand) your e-bike adventure, please ride safely and enjoy every mile. Show courtesy toward fellow cyclists and pedestrians. Encourage your friends to adopt good safety habits and practice proper trail etiquette. Become an advocate for e-bikes and safe biking infrastructure in your community.

Now that you own an e-bike, let it help you expand your horizons. Using the "Helpful Resources" guide that follows, discover new trails to ride and plan a cycling vacation. Consider signing up for an organized bike tour with one of the hundreds of bike-tour companies worldwide. The possibilities are endless.

Want to keep up with the latest in living the e-bike life experience? Do you want to read more inspiring rider profiles? Subscribe (free) to my blog, *This E-Bike Life*, at ThisEBikeLife.com.

In conclusion, hopefully we can all now agree that e-bikes are indeed a great way to put the FUN back into cycling (and life) at any age!

May the wind be with you. Enjoy your ride. 👓

Helpful Resources

As you delve more deeply into the world of cycling and e-bikes, you may find the following online resources helpful. Please visit ThisEBikeLife.com for the most up-to-date cycling resources list.

Author's Websites

⚙ ThisEBikeLife.com
Keep up with e-bike news, cycling, and the e-bike lifestyle

⚙ ThisRetirementLife.com
Learn to live the successful retirement life, including travel, fitness, and finances

Cycling Organizations

Please consider joining one or more cycling organizations and help promote a better, safer future for all cyclists. In addition to this list, there are many more cycling organizations on the local, state or province level. They can use your support to promote better cycling infrastructure, education, and events.

⚙ *Rails To Trails Conservancy:* railstotrails.org

⚙ *League of American Bicyclists:* bikeleague.org

⚙ *People for Bikes:* peopleforbikes.org

⚙ *Velo Canada Bikes:* canadabikes.org

⚙ *Cycling Canada:* cyclingcanada.ca

⚙ *Velo Quebec:* velo.qc.ca

⚙ *Cycling UK:* cycling.org

⚙ *Bike Is Best:* bikeisbest.com

Cycling Organizations, Cont.

- ✷ *ECF (European Cyclists' Federation):* ecf.org
- ✷ *Dutch Cycling Embassy:* dutchcycling.nl/en/
- ✷ *Dutch Cyclists' Union (Fietsersbond):* fietsersbond.nl
- ✷ *Bicycle Network (Australia):* bicyclenetwork.com.au
- ✷ *Cycle (Australia):* cycle.org.au

Bike Trail Information Websites

Be sure to also check local and state/province cycling resources! You can often find state-specific bike organizations with information about favorite trails in their state.

- ✷ *Trail Link (Rails To Trails Conservancy):* traillink.com
- ✷ *AllTrails.com:* alltrails.com
- ✷ *Ontario By Bike:* ontariobybike.ca
- ✷ *Ontario Trails Council:* ontariotrails.on.ca
- ✷ *Bikemap (global):* bikemap.net
- ✷ *EuroVelo (routes and countries)* en.eurovelo.com/#routes-and-countries
- ✷ *Komoot (Europe):* komoot.com
- ✷ *Bicycle Routes & Tours (Europe):* biroto.eu/en/
- ✷ *Cycling UK route finder:* cyclinguk.org/routes
- ✷ *The National Cycle Network (UK)* sustrans.org.uk/national-cycle-network
- ✷ *Bicycle Network (Australia)* bicyclenetwork.com.au/rides-and-events/

Cycling-Specific GPS Apps

- *Map My Ride:* mapmyride.com

- *Ride With GPS:* ridewithgps.com

- *Strava:* strava.com

- *Google Maps:* google.com/maps

- *Komoot:* komoot.com

- *Bikemap:* bikemap.net

- *Ride Spot:* ridespot.org

Other Links To Explore

- *Light Electric Vehicle Association:* levassociation.com

- *Electric Bike Report:* electricbikereport.com

- *National Bicycle Dealer's Association:* nbda.com

- *Bike Index:* bikeindex.org

- *BikeGuard:* myassettag.com/bike/

- *BikeRegister (UK):* bikeregister.com

About The Author

A **Baby Boomer himself,** Dave Hogan writes about living the successful senior life on his blog, This Retirement Life. He encourages older adults to stay active and engaged, with an optimistic outlook and enthusiasm for life.

Some of Dave's fondest childhood memories were made riding his bicycle, and he's never lost that love for cycling. Since discovering e-bikes, Dave is not only cycling more often but also enjoying it more than ever. It's become his passion and joy. He is eager to share the secrets to enjoying the e-bike life with other seniors, both through this book and on his new blog, This E-Bike Life. You can also find Dave writing about retirement living and the e-bike lifestyle on Facebook and other social media sites.

Married with two children and one grandchild, Dave is also a Certified Financial Planner (CFP) and loves to travel. Whenever possible, his e-bike travels with him.

Made in United States
North Haven, CT
15 July 2023